LOGIC MACHINES, DIAGRAMS
AND BOOLEAN ALGEBRA

LOGIC MACHINES, DIAGRAMS AND BOOLEAN ALGEBRA

by Martin Gardner

DOVER PUBLICATIONS, INC., NEW YORK

Published in Canada by General Publishing Company, Ltd., 30 Lesmill Road, Don Mills, Toronto,
Ontario.

This Dover edition, first published in 1968, is an
unabridged and corrected republication of the work
originally published in 1958 by the McGraw-Hill
Book Company under the title *Logic Machines and
Diagrams*. This edition contains a new preface by
the author.

Library of Congress Catalog Card Number: 68-16250

Manufactured in the United States of America
Dover Publications, Inc.
180 Varick Street
New York, N. Y. 10014

for C. G.

Who thinks in a multivalued system all her own.

Preface to the Dover Edition

Since 1958, when this book was first published, general purpose digital computers have increased enormously in speed and memory capacity, and logicians have found increasingly efficient ways of using them. As a result, efforts are no longer being made to design machines for the special purpose of mechanizing symbolic logic. A great deal of research with mechanized logic is still going on, but with few exceptions it is confined to work with available digital computers.

An early electrical machine that I did not know about when I wrote Chapter 8 was a computer designed and built in 1952 by M. E. Maron, then on the staff of the IBM Engineering Research and Development Laboratory, San Jose, California. It was a relay machine that handled up to eight variables in the propositional calculus. The machine was described in what at that time was a confidential technical report of the laboratory, "A Decision Machine for the Sentential Calculus," dated March 6, 1953.

A comprehensive study of Peirce's logic diagrams, *The Existential Graphs of Charles S. Peirce,* provided Don Davis Roberts with his doctorate in philosophy at the University of Illinois in 1963. This dissertation has not been published, but Roberts has examined Peirce's diagrams for the propositional calculus in "The Existential Graphs and Natural Deduction," a contribution to *Studies in the Philosophy of Charles Sanders Peirce, Second Series,* edited by Edward C. Moore and Richard S. Robin (University of Massachusetts Press, 1964). Other references to books and articles published since my book was written will be found in my articles on "Logic Diagrams" and "Logic Machines" in *The Encyclopedia of Philosophy,* edited by Paul Edwards (Macmillan, 1967), Vol. 5, pages 77-83.

Martin Gardner

October, 1967

Preface to the First Edition

A logic machine is a device, electrical or mechanical, designed specifically for solving problems in formal logic. A logic diagram is a geometrical method for doing the same thing. The two fields are closely intertwined, and this book is the first attempt in any language to trace their curious, fascinating histories.

Let no reader imagine that logic machines are merely the playthings of engineers who happen to have a recreational interest in symbolic logic. As we move with terrifying speed into an age of automation, the engineers and mathematicians who design our automata constantly encounter problems that are less mathematical in form than logical. It has been discovered, for example, that symbolic logic can be applied fruitfully to the design and simplification of switching circuits. It has been found that electronic calculators often require elaborate logic units to tell them what steps to follow in tackling certain problems. And in the new field of operations research, annoying situations are constantly arising for which techniques of symbolic logic are surprisingly appropriate. The last chapter of this book suggests some of the ways in which logic machines may play essential roles in coping with the staggering complexities of an automated technology.

Although the book consists for the most part of material drawn from widely separated and often relatively inaccessible books and journals, it also contains much that has not previously been published; at least, not in a layman's language. The reader will find, for example, some unfamiliar uses for the well known Venn circles; an explanation of a novel network diagram for solving problems in the propositional calculus; a popular exposition of the new binary method of handling the calculus; and instructions for making quaint cardboard devices that identify valid syllogisms and show the formal fallacies of invalid ones.

The reader may wonder why so much of the first chapter is devoted to the life and personality of Ramon Lull. The answer is that Ramon's life is much more fascinating than his eccentric logic. Other logicians mentioned in the book may have been far from dull to those who knew them, but with the possible exception of Lord Stanhope, recorded details of their lives are comparatively drab and colorless. Lull's Quixotic career is little known outside of Spain and France, and I make no apologies for introducing the reader to one of the most remarkable tragicomic figures of the Middle Ages.

In choosing symbols for the sentence connectives of the propositional calculus I have adopted those employed by Professor Alonzo Church in Volume I of his *Introduction to Mathematical Logic,* 1956. The symbol for negation, $\sim$, I have used throughout, even though the logic under consideration may be the traditional class logic or its modern formalization as Boolean algebra or the algebra of sets. In class logic it is customary to speak of a "complement" rather than a "negation" and to symbolize it as $\tilde{A}$ or A', but in this book so little notation is used for the class logic that it seemed best to avoid introducing special symbols for it.

I would like to thank George W. Patterson and Wolfe Mays for numerous corrections and suggestions; William Burkhart for valuable assistance in preparing the last two chapters; and my wife for all sorts of help in all sorts of ways.

Martin Gardner

Contents

LOGIC MACHINES, DIAGRAMS
AND BOOLEAN ALGEBRA

1: The Ars Magna of Ramon Lull

Near the city of Palma, on the island of Majorca, largest of the Balearic isles off the eastern coast of Spain, a huge saddle-shaped mountain called Mount Randa rises abruptly from a monotonously level ridge of low hills. It was this desolate mountain that Ramon Lull, Spanish theologian and visionary, climbed in 1274 in search of spiritual refreshment. After many days of fasting and contemplation, so tradition has it, he experienced a divine illumination in which God revealed to him the Great Art by which he might confound infidels and establish with certainty the dogmas of his faith. According to one of many early legends describing this event, the leaves of a small lentiscus bush (a plant still flourishing in the area) became miraculously engraven with letters from the alphabets of many languages. They were the languages in which Lull's Great Art was destined to be taught.

After his illumination, Lull retired to a monastery where he completed his famous *Ars magna,* the first of about forty treatises on the working and application of his eccentric method. It was the earliest attempt in the history of formal logic to employ geometrical diagrams for the purpose of discovering nonmathematical truths, and the first attempt to use a mechanical device—a kind of primitive logic machine—to facilitate the operation of a logic system.

Throughout the remainder of Lull's colorful, quixotic life, and for centuries after his death, his Art was the center of stormy controversy. Franciscan leaders (Lull belonged to a lay order of the movement) looked kindly upon his method, but Dominicans tended to regard it as the work of a madman. Gargantua, in a letter to his son Pantagruel (Rabelais, *Gargantua and Pantagruel,* Book II, Chapter 8), advises him to master astronomy "but dismiss astrology and the divinitory art of Lullius as but vanity and imposture." Francis Bacon similarly ridiculed the Art in two passages of almost identical wording, one in *The Advancement of Learning* (Book II), the other in *De augmentis scientiarum,* a revised and expanded version of the former book. The passage in *De augmentis* (Book VI, Chapter 2) reads as follows:

And yet I must not omit to mention, that some persons, more ostentatious than learned, have laboured about a kind of method not worthy to be called a legitimate method, being rather a method of imposture, which nevertheless would no doubt be very acceptable to certain meddling wits. The object of it is to sprinkle little drops of science about, in such a manner that any sciolist may make some show and ostentation of learning. Such was the Art of Lullius: such the Typocosmy traced out by some; being nothing but a mass and heap of the terms of all arts, to the end that they who are ready with the terms may be thought to understand the arts themselves. Such collections are like a fripper's or broker's shop, that has ends of everything, but nothing of worth.

Swift is thought to have had Lull's Art in mind when he described a machine invented by a professor of Laputa (*Gulliver's Travels,* Part III, Chapter 5). This contrivance was a 20-foot square frame containing hundreds of small cubes linked together by wires. On each face of every cube was written a Laputan word. By turning a crank, the cubes were rotated to produce random combinations of faces. Whenever a few words happened to come together and make sense, they were copied down; then from these broken phrases erudite treatises were composed. In this manner, Swift explained, "the most ignorant person at a reasonable charge, and with a little bodily labour, may write books in philosophy, poetry, politics, law, mathematics, and theology, without the least assistance from genius or study."

On the other hand we find Giordano Bruno, the great Renaissance martyr, speaking of Lull as "omniscient and almost divine," writing fantastically elaborate treatises on the Lullian Art, and teaching it to wealthy noblemen in Venice where it had become a fashionable craze. Later we find young Leibnitz fascinated by

Lull's method. At the age of nineteen he wrote his *Dissertio de arte combinatoria* (Leipzig, 1666), in which he discovers in Lull's work the germ of a universal algebra by which all knowledge, including moral and metaphysical truths, can some day be brought within a single deductive system.[1]* "If controversies were to arise," Leibnitz later declared in an oft-quoted passage, "there would be no more need of disputation between two philosophers than between two accountants. For it would suffice to take their pencils in their hands, to sit down to their slates, and to say to each other (with a friend to witness, if they liked): Let us calculate."

These speculations of Leibnitz's have led many historians to credit Lull with having foreshadowed the development of modern symbolic logic and the empiricist's dream of the "unity of science." Is such credit deserved? Or was Lull's method little more than the fantastic work of a gifted crank, as valueless as the geometric designs of medieval witchcraft? Before explaining and attempting to evaluate Lull's bizarre, now forgotten Art, it will perhaps be of interest to sketch briefly the extraordinary, almost unbelievable career of its inventor.[2]

Ramon Lull was born at Palma, probably in 1232. In his early teens he became a page in the service of King James I of Aragon and soon rose to a position of influence in the court. Although he married young and had two children, his life as a courtier was notoriously dissolute. "The beauty of women, O Lord," he recalled at the age of forty, "has been a plague and tribulation to my eyes, for because of the beauty of women have I been forgetful of Thy great goodness and the beauty of Thy works."

The story of Lull's conversion is the most dramatic of the many picturesque legends about him, and second only to Saint Augustine's as a celebrated example of a conversion following a life of indulgence. It begins with Lull's adulterous passion for a beautiful and pious married woman who failed to respond to his overtures. One day as he was riding a horse down the street he saw the lady enter church for High Mass. Lull galloped into the cathedral after her, only to be tossed out by irate worshippers. Distressed by this scene, the lady resolved to put an end to Lull's campaign. She invited him to her chamber, uncovered the bosom that he had been praising in poems written for her, and revealed a breast partially

---

* Superscript numbers designate references, to be found at the ends of chapters.

consumed by cancer. "See, Ramon," she exclaimed, "the foulness of this body that has won thy affection! How much better hadst thou done to have set thy love on Jesus Christ, of Whom thou mayest have a prize that is eternal!"

Lull retired in great shame and agitation. Shortly after this incident, while he was in his bedroom composing some amorous lyrics, he was startled by a vision of Christ hanging on the Cross. On four later occasions, so the story goes, he tried to complete the verses, and each time was interrupted by the same vision. After a night of remorse and soul searching, he hurried to morning confession as a penitent, dedicated Christian.

Lull's conversion was followed by a burning desire to win nothing less than the entire Moslem world for Christianity. It was an obsession that dominated the remainder of his life and eventually brought about his violent death. As the first necessary step in this ambitious missionary project, Lull began an intensive study of the Arabic language and theology. He purchased a Moorish slave who lived in his home for nine years, giving him instruction in the language. It is said that one day Lull struck the slave in the face after hearing him blaspheme the name of Christ. Soon thereafter the Moor retaliated by attacking Lull with a knife. Lull succeeded in disarming him and the slave was jailed while Lull pondered the type of punishment he should receive. Expecting to be put to death, the Moor hanged himself with the rope that bound him.

Before this unfortunate incident, Lull had managed to finish writing, probably in Arabic, his first book, the *Book of Contemplation*. It is a massive, dull work of several thousand pages that seeks to prove by "necessary reasons" all the major truths of Christianity. Thomas Aquinas had previously drawn a careful distinction between truths of natural theology that he believed could be established by reason, and truths of revelation that could be known only by faith. Lull found this distinction unnecessary. He believed that all the leading dogmas of Christianity, including the trinity and incarnation, could be demonstrated by irrefutable arguments, although there is evidence that he regarded "faith" as a valuable aid in understanding such proofs.

Lull had not yet discovered his Great Art, but the *Book of Contemplation* reveals his early preoccupation with a number symbolism that was characteristic of many scholars of his time. The work is divided into five books in honor of the five wounds of Christ. Forty subdivisions signify the forty days Christ spent in the wilderness. The 366 chapters are designed to be read one a day, the last chapter to be consulted only in leap years. Each chapter has ten paragraphs (the ten commandments); each paragraph has three parts (the trinity), making a total of thirty parts per chapter (the thirty pieces of silver). Angles, triangles, and circles are occasionally introduced as metaphors. Of special interest to modern logicians is Lull's practice of using letters to stand for certain words and phrases so that arguments can be condensed to almost algebraic form. For example, in Chapter 335 he employs a notation of 22 symbols and one encounters passages such as this:

If in Thy three properties there were no difference . . . the demonstration would give the D to the H of the A with the F and the G as it does with the E, and yet the K would not give significance to the H of any defect in the F or the G; but since diversity is shown in the demonstration that the D makes of the E and the F and the G with the I and the K, therefore the H has certain scientific knowledge of Thy holy and glorious Trinity.[3]

There are unmistakable hints of paranoid self-esteem in the value Lull places on his own work in the book's final chapter. It will not only prove to infidels that Christianity is the one true faith, he asserts, but it will also give the reader who follows its teaching a stronger body and mind as well as all the moral virtues. Lull expresses the wish that his book be "disseminated throughout the world," and he assures the reader that he has "neither place nor time sufficient to recount all the ways wherein this book is good and great."

These immodest sentiments are characteristic of most eccentrics who become the founders of cults, and it is not surprising to hear similar sentiments echoed by disciples of the Lullian Art in later centuries. The Old Testament was regarded by many Lullists as the work of God the Father, the New Testament, of God the Son, and the writings of Lull, of God the Holy Spirit. An oft-repeated jingle proclaimed that there had been three wise men in the world— Adam, Solomon, and Ramon:

Tres sabios hubo en el mundo,
Adán, Solomón y Raymundo.

Lull's subsequent writings are extraordinarily numerous although many of them are short and there is much repetition of material and rehashing of old arguments. Some early authorities estimated that he wrote several thousand books. Contemporary scholars consider this an exaggeration, but there is good reason to think that more than two hundred of the works attributed to him are his (the alchemical writings that bear his name are known to be spurious). Most of his books are polemical, seeking to establish Christian doctrines by means of "necessary reasons," or to combat Averroism, Judaism, and other infidel doctrines. Some are encyclopedic surveys of knowledge, such as his 1,300-page *Tree of Science* in which he finds himself forced to speak "of things in an abbreviated fashion." Many of his books are in the form of Socratic dialogues. Others are collections of terse aphorisms, such as his *Book of Proverbs,* a collection of some 6,000 of them. Smaller treatises, most of which concern the application of his Great Art, are devoted to almost every subject matter with which his contemporaries were concerned—astronomy, chemistry, physics, medicine, law, psychology, mnemonics, military tactics, grammar, rhetoric, mathematics, zoology, chivalry, ethics, politics.

Very few of these polemical and pseudo-scientific works have been translated from the original Catalan or Latin versions, and even in Spain they are now almost forgotten. It is as a poet and writer of allegorical romances that Lull is chiefly admired today by his countrymen. His Catalan verse, especially a collection of poems on *The Hundred Names of God*, is reported to be of high quality, and his fictional works contain such startling and imaginative conceptions that they have become an imperishable part of early Spanish literature. Chief of these allegorical books is *Blanquerna,* a kind of Catholic *Pilgrim's Progress*.[4] The protagonist, who closely resembles the author, rises through various levels of church organization until he becomes Pope, only to abandon the office, amid much weeping of cardinals, to become a contemplative hermit.

The Book of the Lover and the Beloved, Lull's best known work, is contained within *Blanquerna* as the supposed product of the hermit's pen.[5] More than any other of Lull's works, this book makes use of the phrases of human love as symbols for divine love—a practice as common in the Moslem literature prior to Lull's time as it was later to become common in the writings of Saint Theresa and other Spanish mystics. Amateur analysts who enjoy looking for erotic symbols will find *The Book of the Lover and the Beloved* a fertile field. All of Lull's passionate temperament finds an outlet here in his descriptions of the intimate relationship of the lover (himself) to his Beloved (Christ).

In Lull's other great work of fantasy, *Felix, or the Book of Marvels*, we find him describing profane love in scenes of such repulsive realism that they would shock even an admirer of Henry Miller's fiction. It is difficult not to believe that Lull's postconversion attitude toward sex had much to do with his vigorous defense of the doctrine of the immaculate conception at a time when it was opposed by the Thomists and of course long before it became church dogma.

After Lull's illumination on Mount Randa, his conviction grew steadily that in his Art he had found a powerful weapon for the conversion of the heathen. The failure of the Crusades had cast doubt on the efficacy of the sword. Lull was convinced that rational argument, aided by his method, might well become God's new means of spreading the faith. The remainder of his life was spent in restless wandering and feverish activity of a missionary and evangelical character. He gave up the large estate he had inherited from his father, distributing his possessions to the poor. His wife and children were abandoned, though he set aside funds for their welfare. He made endless pilgrimages, seeking the aid of popes and princes in the founding of schools and monasteries where his Great Art could be taught along with instruction in heathen languages. The teaching of Oriental languages to missionaries was one of Lull's dominant projects and he is justly regarded as the founder of Oriental studies in European education.

The esoteric character of his Art seems to have exerted a strong magic appeal. Schools and disciples grew so rapidly that in Spain the Lullists became as numerous as the Thomists. Lull even taught on several occasions at the great University of Paris—a signal honor for a man holding no academic degree of any kind. There is an amusing story about his attendance, when at the Sorbonne, of a class taught by Duns Scotus, then a young man fresh from triumphs at Oxford. It seems that Scotus became annoyed by the old man in his audience who persisted in making signs of disagreement with what was being said. As a rebuke, Scotus asked him the exceedingly

elementary question, "What part of speech is 'Lord'?" Lull immediately replied, "The Lord is no part, but the whole," then proceeded to stand and deliver a loud and lengthy oration on the per-
fections of God. The story is believable because Lull always be-
haved as a man possessed by inspired, irrefutable truth.

On three separate occasions Lull made voyages to Africa to clash
verbal swords with Saracen theologians and to preach his views in
the streets of Moslem cities. On the first two visits he barely escaped
with his life. Then at the age of eighty-three, his long beard snow
white and his eyes burning with desire for the crown of martyrdom,
he set sail once more for the northern shore of Africa. In 1315, on
the streets of Bugia, he began expounding in a loud voice the errors
of Moslem faith. The Arabs were understandably vexed, having
twice ousted this stubborn old man from their country. He was
stoned by the angry mob and apparently died on board a Genoese
merchant ship to which his bruised body had been carried.[6] A legend
relates that before he died he had a vision of the American conti-
nent and prophesied that a descendant (i.e., Columbus) of one of
the merchants would some day discover the new world.

". . . no Spaniard since," writes Havelock Ellis (in a chapter on
Lull in his *The Soul of Spain,* 1908), "has ever summed up in his
own person so brilliantly all the qualities that go to the making of
Spain. A lover, a soldier, something of a heretic, much of a saint,
such has ever been the typical Spaniard." Lull's relics now rest in
the chapel of the church of San Francisco, at Palma, where they are
venerated as those of a saint, in spite of the fact that Lull has never
been canonized.

In turning now to an examination of the Great Art itself,[7] it is
impossible, perhaps, to avoid a strong sense of anticlimax. One
wishes it were otherwise. It would be pleasant indeed to discover
that Lull's method had for centuries been unjustly maligned and
that by going directly to the master's own expositions one might
come upon something of value that deserves rescue from the
oblivion into which it has settled. Medieval scholars themselves
sometimes voice such hopes. "We have also excluded the work of
Raymond Lull," writes Philotheus Boehner in the introduction to
his *Medieval Logic,* 1952, "since we have to confess we are not
sufficiently familiar with his peculiar logic to deal with it adequately,
though we suspect that it is much better than the usual evaluation

by historians would lead us to believe." Is this suspicion justified? Or shall we conclude with Etienne Gilson (*History of Christian Philosophy in the Middle Ages,* 1955) that when we today try to use Lull's tables "we come up against the worst difficulties, and one cannot help wondering whether Lull himself was ever able to use them"?

Essentially, Lull's method was as follows. In every branch of knowledge, he believed, there are a small number of simple basic principles or categories that must be assumed without question. By exhausting all possible combinations of these categories we are able to explore all the knowledge that can be understood by our finite minds. To construct tables of possible combinations we call upon the aid of both diagrams and rotating circles. For example, we can list

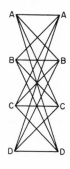

Figure 1.

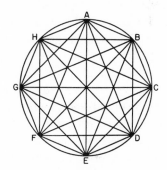

Figure 2.

two sets of categories in two vertical columns (Figure 1), then exhaust all combinations simply by drawing connecting lines as shown. Or we can arrange a set of terms in a circle (Figure 2), draw connecting lines as indicated, then by reading around the circle we quickly obtain a table of two-term permutations.

A third method, and the one in which Lull took the greatest pride, is to place two or more sets of terms on concentric circles as shown in Figure 3. By rotating the inner circle we easily obtain a table of combinations. If there are many sets of terms that we wish to combine, this mechanical method is much more efficient than the others. In Lull's time these circles were made of parchment or metal and painted vivid colors to distinguish different subdivisions of terms. There is no doubt that the use of such strange, multicolored devices threw an impressive aura of mystery around Lull's teachings that greatly intrigued men of little learning, anxious to find a short-cut method of mastering the intricacies of scholasticism. We find a similar appeal today in the "structural differential" invented by Count Alfred Korzybski to illustrate principles of general semantics. Perhaps there is even a touch of the same awe in the reverence

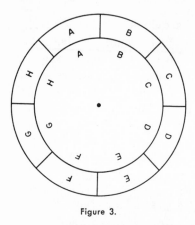

Figure 3.

with which some philosophers view symbolic logic as a tool of philosophical analysis.

Before going into the more complicated aspects of Lull's method, let us give one or two concrete illustrations of how Lull used his circles. The first of his seven basic "figures" is called *A*. The letter "*A*," representing God, is placed in the center of a circle. Around the circumference, inside sixteen compartments (or "camerae" as Lull called them), we

now place the sixteen letters from *B* through *R* (omitting *J* which had no existence in the Latin of the time). These letters stand for sixteen divine attributes—*B* for goodness (*bonitas*), *C* for greatness (*magnitudo*), *D* for eternity (*eternitas*), and so on. By drawing connecting lines (Figure 4) we obtain 240 two-term permutations of the letters, or 120 different combinations that can be arranged in a neat triangular table as shown below.

BC	BD	BE	BF	BG	BH	BI	BK	BL	BM	BN	BO	BP	BQ	BR
	CD	CE	CF	CG	CH	CI	CK	CL	CM	CN	CO	CP	CQ	CR
		DE	DF	DG	DH	DI	DK	DL	DM	DN	DO	DP	DQ	DR
			EF	EG	EH	EI	EK	EL	EM	EN	EO	EP	EQ	ER
				FG	FH	FI	FK	FL	FM	FN	FO	FP	FQ	FR
					GH	GI	GK	GL	GM	GN	GO	GP	GQ	GR
						HI	HK	HL	HM	HN	HO	HP	HQ	HR
							IK	IL	IM	IN	IO	IP	IQ	IR
								KL	KM	KN	KO	KP	KQ	KR
									LM	LN	LO	LP	LQ	LR
										MN	MO	MP	MQ	MR
											NO	NP	NQ	NR
												OP	OQ	OR
													PQ	PR
														QR

Figures 4 to 9, left to right, top to bottom. (From the *Enciclopedia universal ilustrada*, Barcelona, 1923.)

Each of the above combinations tells us an additional truth about God. Thus we learn that His goodness is great (BC) and also eternal (BD), or to take reverse forms of the same pairs of letters, His greatness is good (CB) and likewise His eternity (DB). Reflecting on these combinations will lead us toward the solution of many theological difficulties. For example, we realize that predestination and free will must be combined in some mysterious way beyond our ken; for God is both infinitely wise and infinitely just; therefore He must know every detail of the future, yet at the same time be incapable of withholding from any sinner the privilege of choosing the way of salvation. Lull considered this a demonstration *"per aequiparantium,"* or by means of equivalent relations. Instead of connecting ideas in a cause-and-effect chain, we trace them back to a common origin. Free will and predestination sprout from equally necessary attributes of God, like two twigs growing on branches attached to the trunk of a single tree.

Lull's second figure concerns the soul and is designated by the letter S. Four differently colored squares are used to represent four different states of the soul. The blue square, with corners B, C, D, E, is a normal, healthy soul. The letters signify memory that remembers (B), intellect that knows (C), will that loves (D), and the union of these three faculties (E). The black square $(FGHI)$ is the condition that results when the will hates in a normal fashion as, for example, when it hates sin. This faculty is symbolized by the letter H. F and G stand for the same faculties as B and C, and I for the union of F, G, and H. The red square $(KLMN)$ denotes a condition of soul in which the memory forgets (K), the mind is ignorant (L), and the will hates in an abnormal fashion (M). These three degenerate faculties are united in N. The green square $(OPQR)$ is the square of ambivalence or doubt. R is the union of a memory that retains and forgets (O), a mind that both knows and is ignorant (P), and a will that loves and hates (Q). Lull considered this last state the unhealthiest of the four. We now superimpose the four squares (Figure 5) in such a way that their colored corners form a circle of sixteen letters. This arrangement is more ingenious than one might at first suppose. For in addition to the four corner letters E, I, N, R, which are unions of the other three corners of their respective squares, we also find that the faculties O, P, and Q are unions of the three faculties that precede them as we move clock-

wise around the figure. The circle of sixteen letters can now be rotated within a ring of compartments containing the same faculties
to obtain 136 combinations of faculties.

It would be impossible and profitless to describe all of Lull's
scores of other figures, but perhaps we can convey some notion of
their complexity. His third figure, *T*, concerns relations between
things. Five equilateral triangles of five different colors are superimposed to form a circle of fifteen letters, one letter at each vertex
of a triangle (Figure 6). As in the previous figure, the letters are
in compartments that bear the same color as the polygon for which
they mark the vertices. The meanings of the letters are: God, crea-
ture, and operation (blue triangle); difference, similarity, con-
trariety (green); beginning, middle, end (red); majority, equality,
minority (yellow); affirmation, negation, and doubt (black). Rotating this circle within a ring bearing the same fifteen basic ideas
(broken down into additional elements) gives us 120 combinations,
excluding pairs of the same term (*BB, CC,* etc.) We are thus able
to explore such topics as the beginning and end of God, differences
and similarities of animals, and so on. Lull later found it necessary
to add a second figure *T*, formed of five tinted triangles whose
vertices stand for such concepts as before, after, superior, inferior,
universal, particular, etc. This likewise rotated within a ring to produce 120 combinations. Finally, Lull combined the two sets of
concepts to make thirty in all. By placing them on two circles he
obtained 465 different combinations.

Lull's fourth figure, which he called *V*, deals with the seven
virtues and the seven deadly sins. The fourteen categories are arranged alternately around a circle in red (sinful) and blue (virtu-
ous) compartments (Figure 7). Drawing connecting lines, or rotating the circle within a similarly labeled ring, calls our attention
to such questions as when it might be prudent to become angry,
when lust is the result of slothfulness, and similar matters. Lull's
figure *X* employs eight pairs of traditionally opposed terms, such
as being (*esse*) and privation (*privatio*), arranged in alternate blue
and green compartments (Figure 8). Figures *Y* and *Z* are undivided
circles signifying, respectively, truth and falsehood. Lull used these
letters occasionally in connection with other figures to denote the
truth or falsehood of certain combinations of terms.

This by no means exhausts Lull's use of rotating wheels. Hardly a science or subject matter escapes his analysis by this method. He even produced a book on how preachers could use his Art to discover new topics for sermons, supplying the reader with 100 sample sermons produced by his spinning wheels! In every case the technique is the same: find the basic elements, then combine them mechanically with themselves or with the elements of other figures. Dozens of his books deal with applications of the Art, introducing endless small variations of terminology and symbols. Some of these works are introductions to more comprehensive treatises. Some are brief, popular versions for less intellectual readers who find it hard to comprehend the more involved figures. For example, the categories of certain basic figures are reduced from sixteen to nine (see Figure 9). These simpler ninefold circles are the ones encountered in the writings of Bruno, Kircher, and other Renaissance Lullists, in Hegel's description of the Art (*Lectures on the History of Philosophy,* Vol. 3), and in most modern histories of thought that find space for Lull's method. Two of Lull's treatises on his Art are written entirely in Catalan verse.

One of Lull's ninefold circles is concerned with objects of knowledge—God, angel, heaven, man, the imagination, the sensitive, the negative, the elementary, and the instrumental. Another asks the nine questions—whether? what? whence? why? how great? of what kind? when? where? and how? Many of Lull's books devote considerable space to questions suggested by these and similar circles. *The Book of the Ascent and Descent of the Intellect*, using a twelvefold and a fivefold circle in application to eight categories (stone, flame, plant, animal, man, heaven, angel, God) considers such scientific posers as: Where does the flame go when a candle is put out? Why does rue strengthen the eyes and onions weaken them? Where does the cold go when a stone is warmed?

In another interesting work Lull uses his Art to explain to a hermit the meaning of some of the *Sentences* of Peter Lombard. The book takes up such typical medieval problems as: Could Adam and Eve have cohabited before they ate their first food? If a child is slain in the womb of a martyred mother, will it be saved by a baptism of blood? How do angels speak to each other? How do angels pass from one place to another in an instant of time? Can God make matter without form? Can He damn Peter and save Judas? Can a fallen angel repent? In one book, the *Tree of Science*, over four thousand such questions are raised! Sometimes Lull gives the combination of terms in which the answer may be found, together with a fully reasoned commentary. Sometimes he merely indicates the figures to be used, letting the reader find the right combinations for himself. At other times he leaves the question entirely unanswered.

The number of concentric circles to be used in the same figure varies from time to time—two or three being the most common. The method reaches its climax in a varicolored metal device called the *figura universalis* which has no less than fourteen concentric circles! The mind reels at the number and complexity of topics that can be explored by this fantastic instrument.

Before passing on to an evaluation of Lull's method, it should be mentioned that he also frequently employed the diagrammatic device of the tree to indicate subdivisions of genera and species. For Lull it was both an illustrative and a mnemonic device. His *Principles of Medicine,* for example, pictures his subject matter as a tree with four roots (the four humors) and two trunks (ancient and modern medicine). The trunks branch off into various boughs on which flowers bloom, each flower having a symbolic meaning (air, exercise, food, sleep, etc.). Colored triangles, squares, and other Lullian figures also are attached to the branches.

None of Lull's scientific writings, least of all his medical works, added to the scientific knowledge of his time. In such respects he was neither ahead nor behind his contemporaries. Alchemy and geomancy he rejected as worthless. Necromancy, or the art of communicating with the dead, he accepted in a sense common in his day and still surviving in the attitude of many orthodox churchmen; miraculous results are not denied, but they are regarded as demonic in origin. Lull even used the success of necromancers as a kind of proof of the existence of God. The fallen angels could not exist, he argued, if God had not created them.

There is no doubt about Lull's complete acceptance of astrology. His so-called astronomical writings actually are astrological, showing how his circles can be used to reveal various favorable and unfavorable combinations of planets within the signs of the zodiac. In one of his books he applies astrology to medicine. By means of the Art he obtains sixteen combinations of the four elements (earth, air, fire, water) and the four properties (hot, cold, moist, dry).

These are then combined in various ways with the signs of the zodiac to answer medical questions concerning diet, evacuation, preparation of medicines, fevers, color of urine, and so on.

There is no indication that Ramon Lull, the Doctor Illuminatus as he was later called, ever seriously doubted that his Art was the product of divine illumination. But one remarkable poem, the *Desconort* ("Disconsolateness"), suggests that at times he may have been tormented by the thought that possibly his Art was worthless. The poem is ingeniously constructed of sixty-nine stanzas, each consisting of twelve lines that end in the same rhyme. It opens with Lull's bitter reflections on his failure for the past thirty years to achieve any of his missionary projects. Seeking consolation in the woods, he comes upon the inevitable hermit and pours out to him the nature of his sorrows. He is a lonely, neglected man. People laugh at him and call him a fool. His great Art is ridiculed and ignored. Instead of sympathizing, the hermit tries to prove to Ramon that he deserves this ridicule. If his books on the Art are read by men "as fast as a cat that runs through burning coals," perhaps this is because the dogmas of the church cannot be demonstrated by reason. If they could be, then what merit would there be in believing them? In addition, the hermit argues, if Lull's method is so valuable, how is it that the ancient philosophers never thought of it? And if it truly comes from God, what reason has he to fear it will ever be lost?

Lull replies so eloquently to these objections that we soon find the hermit begging forgiveness for all he has said, offering to join Ramon in his labors, and even weeping because he had not learned the Art earlier in life!

Perhaps the most striking illustration of how greatly Lull valued his method is the legend of how he happened to join the third order of Franciscans. He had made all necessary arrangements for his first missionary trip to North Africa, but at the last moment, tormented by doubts and fears of imprisonment and death, he allowed the boat to sail without him. This precipitated a mental breakdown that threw him into a state of profound depression. He was carried into a Dominican church and while praying there he saw a light like a star and heard a voice speak from above: "Within this order thou shalt be saved." Lull hesitated to join the order because he knew the Dominicans had little interest in his Art whereas the

Franciscans had found it of value. A second time the voice spoke from the light, this time threateningly: "And did I not tell thee that only in the order of the Preachers thou wouldst find salvation?" Lull finally decided it would be better to undergo personal damnation than risk the loss of his Art whereby others might be saved. Ignoring the vision, he joined the Franciscans.

It is clear from Lull's writings that he thought of his method as possessing many values. The diagrams and circles aid the understanding by making it easy to visualize the elements of a given argument. They have considerable mnemonic value, an aspect of his Art that appealed strongly to Lull's Renaissance admirers. They have rhetorical value, not only arousing interest by their picturesque, cabalistic character, but also aiding in the demonstration of proofs and the teaching of doctrines. It is an investigative and inventive art. When ideas are combined in all possible ways, the new combinations start the mind thinking along novel channels and one is led to discover fresh truths and arguments, or to make new inventions. Finally, the Art possesses a kind of deductive power.

Lull did not, however, regard his method as a substitute for the formal logic of Aristotle and the schoolmen. He was thoroughly familiar with traditional logic and his writings even include the popular medieval diagrams of immediate inference and the various syllogistic figures and moods. He certainly did not think that the mere juxtaposition of terms provided in themselves a proof by "necessary reasons." He did think, however, that by the mechanical combination of terms one could discover the necessary building blocks out of which valid arguments could then be constructed. Like his colleagues among the schoolmen, he was convinced that each branch of knowledge rested on a relatively few, self-evident principles which formed the structure of all knowledge in the same way that geometrical theorems were formed out of basic axioms. It was natural for him to suppose that by exhausting the combinations of such principles one might thereby explore all possible structures of truth and so obtain universal knowledge.

There is a sense, of course, in which Lull's method of exploration does possess a formal deductive character. If we wish to exhaust the possible combinations of given sets of terms, then Lull's method obviously will do this for us in an irrefutable way. Considered mathematically, the technique is sound, though even in its day it was essentially trivial. Tabulating combinations of terms was certainly a familiar process to mathematicians as far back as the Greeks, and it would be surprising indeed if no one before Lull had thought of using movable circles as a device for obtaining such tables. Lull's mistake, in large part a product of the philosophic temper of his age, was to suppose that his combinatorial method had useful application to subject matters where today we see clearly that it does not apply. Not only is there a distressing lack of "analytic" structure in areas of knowledge outside of logic and mathematics, there is not even agreement on what to regard as the most primitive, "self-evident" principles in any given subject matter. Lull naturally chose for his categories those that were implicit in the dogmas and opinions he wished to establish. The result, as Chesterton might have said, was that Lull's circles led him in most cases into proofs that were circular. Other schoolmen were of course often guilty of question begging, but it was Lull's peculiar distinction to base this type of reasoning on such an artificial, mechanical technique that it amounted virtually to a satire of scholasticism, a sort of hilarious caricature of medieval argumentation.

We have mentioned earlier that it was Leibnitz who first saw in Lull's method the possibility of applying it to formal logic.[8] For example, in his *Dissertio de arte combinatoria* Leibnitz constructs an exhaustive table of all possible combinations of premises and conclusions in the traditional syllogism. The false syllogisms are then eliminated, leaving no doubt as to the number of valid ones, though of course revealing nothing that was not perfectly familiar to Aristotle. A somewhat similar technique of elimination was used by Jevons (as we shall see in Chapter 5) in his "logical alphabet" and his logic machine, and is used today in the construction of matrix tables for problems in symbolic logic. Like Lull, however, Leibnitz failed to see how restricted was the application of such a technique, and his vision of reducing all knowledge to composite terms built up out of simple elements and capable of being manipulated like mathematical symbols is certainly as wildly visionary as Lull's similar dream. It is only in the dimmest sense that Leibnitz can be said to anticipate modern symbolic logic. In Lull's case the anticipation is so remote that it scarcely deserves mention.

Still, there is something to be said for certain limited applications of Lull's circles, though it must be confessed that the applications are to subject matters which Lull would have considered frivolous. For example, parents seeking a first and middle name for a newborn baby might find it useful to write all acceptable first names in one circle and acceptable middle names on a larger circle, then rotate the inner circle to explore the possible combinations. Ancient coding and decoding devices for secret ciphers make use of Lullian-type wheels. Artists and decorators sometimes employ color wheels for exploring color combinations. Anagram puzzles often can be solved quickly by using Lullian circles to permute the required letters. A cardboard toy for children consists of a rotating circle with animal pictures around the circumference, half of each animal on the circle and half on the sheet to which the wheel is fastened. Turning the circle produces amusing combinations—a giraffe's head on the body of a hippopotamus, and so on. One thinks also of Sam Loyd's famous "Get off the earth" paradox. Renan once described Lull's circles as "magic," but in turning Loyd's wheel the picture of an entire Chinese warrior is made to vanish before your very eyes.[9] It is amusing to imagine how Lull would have analyzed Loyd's paradox, for his aptitude for mathematical thinking was not very high.

Even closer to the spirit of Lull's method is a device that was sold to fiction writers many years ago and titled, if I remember correctly, the "Plot Genii." By turning concentric circles one could obtain different combinations of plot elements. (One suspects that Aldous Huxley constructed his early novels with the aid of wheels bearing different neurotic types. He simply spun the circles until he found an amusing and explosive combination of house guests.) Mention also should be made of the book called *Plotto,* privately published in Battle Creek, Mich., 1928, by William Wallace Cook, a prolific writer of potboilers. Although *Plotto* did not use spinning wheels, it was essentially Lullian in its technique of combining plot elements, and apparently there were many writers willing to pay the seventy-five dollar price originally asked by the author.

In current philosophy one occasionally comes upon notions for which a Lullian device might be appropriate. For instance, Charles Morris tells us that a given sign (e.g., a word) can be analyzed in terms of three kinds of meaning: syntactic, semantic, and pragmatic. Each meaning in turn has a syntactic, semantic, and pragmatic meaning, and this threefold analysis can be carried on indefinitely. To dramatize this dialectical process one might use a series of rotating circles, each bearing the words "syntactic," "semantic," and "pragmatic," with the letter S in the center of the inner wheel to signify the sign being analyzed.

In science there also are rare occasions when a Lullian technique might prove useful. The tree diagram is certainly a convenient way to picture evolution. The periodic table can be considered a kind of Lullian chart that exhausts all permissible combinations of certain primitive principles and by means of which chemists have been able to predict the properties of elements before they were discovered. Lull's crude anticipation was a circle bearing the four traditional elements and rotated within a ring similarly labeled.

There may even be times when an inventor or researcher might find movable circles an aid. Experimental situations often call for a testing of all possible combinations of a limited number of substances or techniques. What is invention, after all, except the knack of finding new and useful combinations of old principles? When Thomas Edison systematically tested almost every available substance as a filament for his light bulb, he was following a process that Lull would probably have considered an extension of his method. One American scientist, an acoustical engineer and semiprofessional magician, Dariel Fitzkee, actually published in 1944 a book called *The Trick Brain* in which he explains a technique for combining ideas in Lullian fashion for the purpose of inventing new magic tricks.

If the reader will take the trouble to construct some Lullian circles related to a subject matter of special interest to himself, and play with them for a while, he will find it an effective way of getting close to Lull's mind. There is an undeniable fascination in twisting the wheels and letting the mind dwell on the strange combinations that turn up. Something of the mood of medieval Lullism begins to pervade the room and one comprehends for the first time why the Lullian cult persisted for so many centuries.

For persist it did.[10] Fifty years after Lull's death it was strong enough to provoke a vigorous campaign against Lullism, led by Dominican inquisitors. They succeeded in having Lull condemned as a heretic by a papal bull, though later church officials decided that the bull had been a forgery. Lullist schools, supported chiefly by Franciscans, flourished throughout the late Middle Ages and Renaissance, mostly in Spain but also in other parts of Europe. We have already cited Bruno's intense interest in the Art. The great ex-Dominican considered Lull's method divinely inspired though badly applied. For example, he thought Lull mad to suppose that such truths of faith as the incarnation and trinity could be established by necessary reasons. Bruno's first and last published works, as well as many in between, were devoted to correcting and improving the method, notably *The Compendious Building and Completion of the Lullian Art*.

In 1923 the British Museum acquired a portable sundial and compass made in Rome in 1593 in the form of a book (Figure 10).

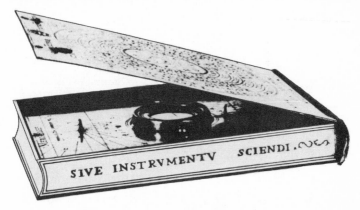

Figure 10. Sixteenth-century portable sundial engraved with Lullian figures. (From *Archaeologia*, Oxford, 1925.)

On the front and back of the two gilt copper "covers" are engraved the Lullian circles shown in Figures 11 to 14. For an explanation of these circles the reader is referred to O. M. Dalton's article, "A Portable Dial in the Form of a Book, with Figures Derived from Ramon Lul," *Archaeologia*, Vol. 74, second series, Oxford, 1925, pp. 89–102.

The seven smaller diagrams in Figure 12 are all from Lull's writings [11] and perhaps worth a few comments. The square in the upper left corner is designed to show how the mind can conceive of geometrical truths not apparent to the senses. A diagonal divides the square into two large triangles, one of which is subdivided to make the smaller triangles *B* and *C*. Each triangle contains three angles; so that our senses immediately perceive nine angles in all. However, we can easily imagine the large triangle to be subdi-

1. Upper cover, outer side

2. Upper cover, inner side

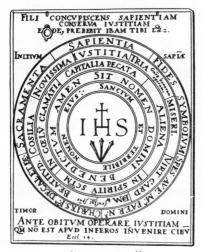

3. Lower cover, outer side

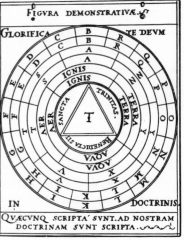

4. Lower cover, inner side

Figures 11 to 14, left to right, top to bottom. Circles used by Renaissance Lullists. (From *Archaeologia*, Oxford, 1925.)

vided also, making four small triangles or twelve angles in all. The three additional angles exist "potentially" in triangle A. We do not see them with our eyes, but we can see them with our imagination. In this way our intellect, aided by imagination, arrives at new geometrical truths.

The top right square is designed to prove that there is only one universe rather than a plurality of worlds. The two circles represent two universes. We see at once that certain parts of A and B are nearer to each other than other parts of A and B. But, Lull argues, "far" and "near" are meaningless concepts if nothing whatever exists in the space between A and B. We are forced to conclude that two universes are impossible.

I think what Lull means here, put in modern terms, is that we cannot conceive of two universes without supposing some sort of space-time relation between them, but once we relate them, we bring them into a common manifold; so we can no longer regard them as separate universes. Lull qualifies this by saying that his argument applies only to actual physical existence, not to higher realms of being which God could create at will, since His power is infinite.

The four intersecting circles are interesting because they anticipate in a vague way the use of circles to represent classes in the diagrammatic methods of Euler and Venn (to be discussed in the next chapter). The four letters which label the circles stand for *Esse* (being), *Unum* (the one), *Verum* (the true), and *Bonum* (the good). *Unum, verum,* and *bonum* are the traditional three "transcendentales" of scholastic philosophy. The overlapping of the circles indicates that the four qualities are inseparable. Nothing can exist without possessing unity, truth, and goodness.

The circle divided into three sectors represents the created universe, but I am not sure of the meaning of the letters which apparently signify the parts. The lower left square illustrates a practical problem in navigation. It involves a ship sailing east, but forced to travel in a strong north wind. The lower right square is clearly a Lullian table displaying the twelve permutations of $ABCD$ taken two letters at a time.

The remaining diagram, at the middle of the bottom, is a primitive method of squaring the circle and one fairly common in medieval pseudo-mathematical works. We first inscribe a square and circumscribe a square; then we draw a third square midway between the other two. This third square, Lull mistakenly asserts, has a perimeter equal to the circumference of the circle as well as an area equal to the circle's area. Lull's discussion of this figure (in his *Ars magna et ultima*) reveals how far behind he was of the geometry of his time.[12] His method does not provide even a close approximation of the perimeter or area of the desired square.[13]

Books on the Lullian art proliferated throughout the seventeenth century, many of them carrying inserted sheets of circles to be cut out, or actual rotating circles with centers attached permanently to the page. Wildly exaggerated claims were made for the method. The German Jesuit Athanasius Kircher (1601–1680), scientist, mathematician, cryptographer, and student of Egyptian hieroglyphics, was also a confirmed Lullist. He published in Amsterdam in 1669 a huge tome of nearly 500 pages titled *Ars magna sciendi sive combinatoria*. It abounds with Lullian figures and circles bearing ingenious pictographic symbols of his own devising.[14]

The eighteenth century witnessed renewed opposition to Lull's teachings in Majorca and the publication of many Spanish books and pamphlets either attacking or defending him. Benito Feyjóo, in the second volume of his *Cartas eruditas y curiosas* ("Letters erudite and curious"), ridiculed Lull's art so effectively that he provoked a two-volume reply in 1749–1750 by the Cistercian monk Antonio Raymundo Pasqual, a professor of philosophy at the Lullian University of Majorca. This was followed in 1778 by Pasqual's *Vinciciae Lullianae,* an important early biography and defense of Lull. The nineteenth and twentieth centuries saw a gradual decline of interest in the Art and a corresponding increase of attention toward Lull as a poet and mystic. A periodical devoted to Lullian studies, the *Revista luliana,* flourished from 1901 to 1905. Today there are many enthusiastic admirers of Lull in Majorca and other parts of Spain, though the practice of his Art has all but completely vanished.

The Church has approved Lull's beatification, but there seems little likelihood he will ever be canonized. There are three principal reasons. His books contain much that may be considered heretical. His martyrdom seems to have been provoked by such rash behavior that it takes on the coloration of a suicide. And finally, his insistence on the divine origin of his Art and his constant emphasis on its indispensability as a tool for the conversion of infidels lends a touch of madness, certainly of the fantastic, to Lull's personality.

Lull himself was fully aware that his life was a fantastic one. He even wrote a book called *The Dispute of a Cleric and Ramon the Fantastic* in which he and a priest each try to prove that the other has had the most preposterous life. At other times he speaks of himself as "Ramon the Fool." He was indeed a Spanish *joglar* of the faith, a troubadour who sang his passionate love songs to his Beloved and twirled his colored circles as a juggler twirls his colored plates, more to the amusement or annoyance of his countrymen than to their edification. No one need regret that the controversy over his Great Art has at last been laid to rest and that the world is free to admire Lull as the first great writer in the Catalan tongue, and a religious eccentric unique in medieval Spanish history.

References

1. In later years Leibnitz was often critical of Lull, but he always regarded as sound the basic project sketched in his *Dissertio de arte combinatoria.* In a letter written in 1714 he makes the following comments:
   "When I was young, I found pleasure in the Lullian art, yet I thought also that I found some defects in it, and I said something about these in a little schoolboyish essay called *On the Art of Combinations,* published in 1666, and later reprinted without my permission. But I do not readily disdain anything—except the arts of divination, which are nothing but pure cheating—and I have found something valuable, too, in the art of Lully and in the *Digestum sapientiae* of the Capuchin, Father Ives, which pleased me greatly because he found a way to apply Lully's generalities to useful particular problems. But it seems to me that Descartes had a profundity of an entirely different level." (*Gottfried Wilhelm von Leibniz: Philosophical Papers and Letters,* edited and translated by Leroy E. Loemker, University of Chicago Press, 1956, Vol. 2, p. 1067.)
2. In sketching Lull's life I have relied almost entirely on E. Allison Peers's magnificent biography, *Ramon Lull,* London, 1929, the only adequate study of Lull in English. An earlier and briefer biography, *Raymond Lull, the Illuminated Doctor,* was published in London, 1904, by W. T. A. Barber, who also contributed an informative article on Lull to the *Encyclopedia of Religion and Ethics.* Other English references worth noting are: Otto Zöckler's article in the *Religious Encyclopedia;* William Turner's article in the *Catholic Encyclopedia;* George Sarton, *Introduction to the History of Science,* 1931, Vol. II, pp. 900 ff.; and Lynn Thorndike, *A History of Magic and Experimental Science,* 1923, Vol. II, pp. 862 ff.
   A voluminous bibliography of Lull's works, with short summaries of each, may be found in the *Histoire littéraire de la France,* Paris, 1885, Vol. XXIX, pp. 1–386, an indispensable reference for students of Lull. There also is an excellent article on Lull by P. Ephrem Langpré in Vol. IX of the *Dictionnaire*

de théologie Catholique, Paris, 1927. It is interesting to note that a 420-page novel based on the life of Lull, *Le Docteur illumine,* by Lucien Graux, appeared in Paris in 1927.

The most accessible Spanish references are the articles on Lull in the *Enciclopedia universal ilustrada,* Barcelona, 1923, and Vol. 1 of *Historia de la filosofía española,* by Tomás Carreras y Artau, Madrid, 1939.

3. Quoted by Peers, *op. cit.,* p. 64.
4. An English translation by Peers was published in 1926.
5. Separately issued in English translation by Peers in 1923.
6. Lull's death is the basis of a short story by Aldous Huxley, "The Death of Lully," in his book *Limbo,* 1921.
7. The only satisfactory description in English of Lull's method is in Vol. 1 of Johann Erdmann's *History of Philosophy,* English translation, London, 1910. There are no English editions of any of Lull's books dealing with his Art. Peers's biography may be consulted for a list of Latin and Spanish editions of Lull's writings.
8. See *La logique de Leibniz,* by Louis Couturat, Paris, 1901, chap. IV, and *Leibniz,* by Ruth Lydia Shaw, London, 1954, chap. VIII.
9. Chapter 7 of my *Mathematics, Magic, and Mystery,* 1956, contains a reproduction and analysis of Loyd's "Get off the earth" puzzle and several related paradoxes.
10. *Historia del Lulisme,* by Joan Avinyó, a history of Lullism to the eighteenth century, was published in Barcelona in 1925. My quick survey of Lullism draws largely on Peers's account.
11. With the exception of the table of permutations, all these diagrams are reproduced and discussed in Zetzner's one-volume Latin edition of several of Lull's works, first printed in Strasbourg, 1598.
12. Bryson of Heraclea, a pupil of Socrates, had recognized that, if you keep increasing the number of sides of the inscribed and circumscribed polygons, you get increasingly closer approximations of the circle. It was through applying this method of limits that Archimedes was able to conclude that pi was somewhere between 3.141 and 3.142.

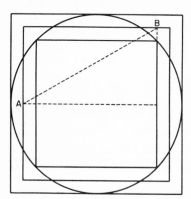

Figure 15.

13. It has been called to my attention that, if a diagonal line *AB* is drawn on Lull's figure as shown in Figure 15, it gives an extremely good approximation to the side of a square with an area equal to the area of the circle.
14. Kircher's enormous books are fascinating mixtures of science and nonsense. He seems to have anticipated motion pictures by constructing a magic lantern that threw images on a screen in fairly rapid succession to illustrate such events as the ascension of Christ. He invented (as did Leibnitz) an early calculating machine. On the other hand, he devoted a 250-page treatise to details in the construction of Noah's Ark!

Kircher's work on the Lullian art appeared three years after Leibnitz's youthful treatise of similar title (see reference 1). Leibnitz later wrote that he had hoped to find important matters discussed in Kircher's book but was disappointed to discover that it "had merely revived the Lullian art or something similar to it, but that the author had not even dreamed of the true analysis of human thoughts." (Vol. 1, p. 352, of the edition of Leibnitz's papers and letters cited in reference 1.)

2: Logic Diagrams

Alogic diagram is a two-dimensional geometric figure with spatial relations that are isomorphic with the structure of a logical statement. These spatial relations are usually of a topological character, which is not surprising in view of the fact that logic relations are the primitive relations underlying all deductive reasoning and topological properties are, in a sense, the most fundamental properties of spatial structures. Logic diagrams stand in the same relation to logical algebras as the graphs of curves stand in relation to their algebraic formulas; they are simply other ways of symbolizing the same basic structure.

There has always been, and continues to be, a curious tendency among certain logicians to peer down their noses at logic diagrams as though they were barbaric attempts to picture a structure more appropriately represented by words or notational symbols. One might as well look upon the graph of a parabola as somehow of a lower status than the algebraic equation that produces it. Clearly, the parabola and its formula are simply two different ways of asserting the same thing. The parabola is a spatial way of representing an equation; the equation is an algebraic expression of a parabola. It would be foolish to ask which of the two, considered in itself, is superior to the other. Each has its uses, and it is only in reference to human purposes that we can speak of their relative merits or defects.

In logic, a good diagram has several virtues. Many individuals think with far greater ease when they can visualize an argument pictorially, and a diagram often makes clear to them a matter which they might have difficulty grasping in verbal or algebraic form. For this reason, logic diagrams are extremely valuable pedagogic devices. Moreover, a good diagrammatic method is capable of solving certain logic problems in the same efficient way that a graph may be used for the solution of certain equations. True—algebraic methods of dealing with logic problems are usually faster and more reliable, but this is not always the case, and even when it is, the diagram affords a convenient technique for checking results obtained by other means. Finally, the study of logic diagrams is an intensely interesting and relatively unexplored field. It is closely allied with the rapidly growing subject of topology, and its kinship with the network theory underlying the construction of electronic calculators and other automata suggests that it may have contributions to make in the near future that will be much more than trivial or recreational.

Historically, the first logic diagrams probably expressed statements in what today is called the logic of relations. The tree figure, for example, was certainly known to Aristotle as a handy way of picturing successive subdivisions of matter and form, or genera and species. The so-called tree of Porphyry, so often found in medieval and Renaissance logics, is one example of this type of diagram. In the previous chapter we spoke of Lull's fondness for the tree device, and its useful application today in depicting such structures as the evolutionary history of plants and animals. The genealogical family tree (actually an interlocking of many separate tree figures) is another example. Drawing such a tree is often the quickest and easiest way to determine a relationship between two people, another way of saying that it is a useful tool for solving a certain type of logic problem.

Statements involving transitive asymmetric relations, such as "taller than," "heavier than," "to the left of," and so on, are so easily diagramed that the technique must have been a familiar one to the ancients, certainly so obvious as to be of little interest to us here. Likewise, we may pass quickly over such popular medieval devices as the various "squares of opposition" (for showing certain relations of immediate inference from one class proposition to another) as well as the "pons asinorum" of Petrus Tartaretus. The latter is a geometrical method of finding the middle terms of an

30 Logic Machines, Diagrams, and Boolean Algebra

argument. Jean Buridan, the fourteenth century French nominalist, was much concerned in his logical writings with finding middle terms, and his method became known as a "pons asinorum" ("bridge of asses") because it helped dull-witted students pass over from the major and minor terms to the middle ones. The phrase later became attached to the elaborate hexagonal figure that apparently first appeared in a fifteenth century work on logic by Petrus Tartaretus. (The interested reader will find the figure reproduced and explained in Karl Prantl's *Geschichte der Logik im Abendlande*, Leipzig, 1855–1870, Vol. 4, p. 206.) In later centuries, pons asinorum became a common phrase for Euclid's fifth proposition proving the base angles of an isosceles triangle to be equal, a bridge that only stupid students had difficulty in crossing.

On a slightly higher "iconic" level (Charles Peirce's term for the resemblance of a sign to the thing it signifies) are the three diagrams pictured in Figure 16. These are designed to exhibit the rela-

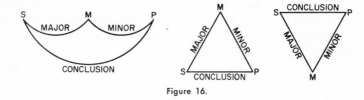

Figure 16.

tions between terms in the first three figures of a syllogism. William Hamilton, in *Discussions on Philosophy and Literature,* 1866, p. 666, traces their origin back to the fifth century of the Christian era. They are to be found in Lull's logical works and innumerable other medieval treatises. Giordano Bruno, in a commentary on Lull's system, superimposes the three figures and surrounds them

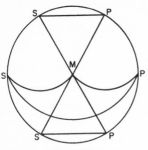

Figure 17.

with a circle to obtain the mysterious diagram shown in Figure 17. Beyond showing that the conclusion of a syllogism expresses a relation between two terms that is obtained by traversing another route that leads through a middle term, these figures have almost no iconic value and need not detain us further.

The first important step toward a diagrammatic method sufficiently iconic to be serviceable as a tool for solving problems of class logic was the use of a simple closed curve to represent a class. We have seen how Lull employed four intersecting circles to show that existence possesses the transcendental predicates of truth, goodness, and unity. The use of three intersecting circles to illustrate the unity of the three parts of the godhead was also a common medieval figure. It is difficult to say who was the first to use a circle for representing actual class propositions and syllogisms. Alonzo Church, in his contribution to the section on logic in the fourteenth edition of the Encyclopaedia Britannica, mentions the early use of circles for this purpose by Johann Christoph Sturm (in his *Universalia Euclidea,* 1661), Leibnitz, and Johann Christian Lange (in his *Nucleus logicae Weisianae*, 1712). There is no doubt, however, that it was Leonhard Euler, the brilliant Swiss mathematician, who was responsible for introducing them into the history of logical analysis. He first described them in seven letters, the earliest written in 1761, and all printed in his *Lettres à une princesse d'Allemagne,* Vol. 2, 1772, letters 102 to 108. Here for the first time we meet with a geometrical system that will not only represent class statements and syllogisms in a highly isomorphic manner, but also can be manipulated for the actual solution of problems in class logic.

Euler's method will not be explained here because it has been supplanted by the much more efficient method developed by the English logician John Venn (1834–1923), lecturer in the moral sciences, Cambridge University. Venn's *Symbolic Logic,* revised second edition, 1894, may be consulted for a clear exposition of Euler's system as well as an analysis of its defects. In the last chapter of Venn's book one will also find a compact survey of the history of class logic diagrams, a survey from which much of the foregoing data have been drawn. This chapter may also be consulted for interesting anticipations of Euler's system, as well as later variations that employ triangles, squares, and other parallelograms. Since class inclusion is not concerned with numerical quantity, any closed curve topologically equivalent to a circle can be used. Of special interest is a linear method of diagraming, closely allied to the Euler circles, that was developed by Euler's contemporary, the German mathematician Johann Heinrich Lambert, and explained in his *Neues Organon,* 1764.[1]

All these methods, including Euler's, had severe limitations. They were elegantly overcome by Venn's system of intersecting circles, which explains why they have dropped into such complete oblivion. Venn first published his method in an article, "On the Diagrammatic and Mechanical Representation of Propositions and Reasonings," *Philosophical Magazine,* July, 1880. The technique is discussed more fully in his book cited above.

There are several aspects of the "Venn circles" that will be of interest to consider in this chapter, but before doing so it will be expedient to digress for a moment and consider briefly the nature of the syllogism. This discussion will have an important bearing on much that follows, as well as make it easier to understand the syllogism-solving machines to be described in later chapters.

Although Aristotle defined the syllogism broadly as any formal argument in which the conclusion follows necessarily from the premises, his own analysis centers on a very specific type of argument. He had observed that statements often took a subject-predicate form with the subject preceded by such qualifying adjectives as "all," "some," "none." The four most common statements of this type, traditionally labeled *A, E, I,* and *O,* are:

> *A*—All *S* is *P* (universal affirmative)
> *E*—No *S* is *P* (universal negative)
> *I*—Some *S* is *P* (particular affirmative)
> *O*—Some *S* is not *P* (particular negative)

Aristotle further observed that a statement of this sort could be correctly inferred from two statements of similar form, one relating the subject (*S*) of the conclusion to a "middle term" (*M*), the other relating the middle term to the predicate (*P*) of the conclusion. For example:

> All *M* is *P*
> All *S* is *M*
> All *S* is *P*

It was this specific type of "mediate inference" by way of a middle term that Aristotle was the first to dissect and analyze, and to which the term "syllogism" soon became firmly attached. Aristotle's way of classifying syllogisms was to divide them into three "figures" depending on the "width" or "extension" of the middle term (i.e., whether it concerned all or part of its class) as compared with the width of the other terms. Later logicians, classifying syllogisms by the *position* of the middle term, added a fourth figure. Each figure in turn was divided into "moods," each mood being a different combination of the four basic statements. The syllogism cited above is in the mood *AAA* of the first figure. Medieval logicians gave a mnemonic name to each valid syllogism, the vowels of the name corresponding to the three assertions of the syllogism. In this case the mnemonic name is *Barbara*.

If we assume that every term in a syllogism stands for a class that actually has members (e.g., when a premise asserts that "All unicorns have only one horn," we must assume that there are such things as unicorns), then 24 of the 256 combinations are valid inferences. Only 15 are valid if we adopt the narrower view that a class qualified by "all" or "none" may be "empty"; that is, it may or may not have members.

It is true of course that Aristotle and his medieval followers greatly exaggerated the importance of the syllogism. In the light of modern symbolic logic we now see it as a restricted form of class-inclusion inference seldom encountered in everyday thought or speech. The following quotation from Bertrand Russell's *An Outline of Philosophy*, 1927, is a well-known expression of the disdain a modern logician feels for this ancient logical form:

> This form of inference does actually occur, though very rarely. The only instance I have ever heard of was supplied by Dr. F. C. S. Schiller. He once produced a comic number of the philosophical periodical *Mind*, and sent copies to various philosophers, among others to a certain German, who was much puzzled by the advertisements. But at last he argued: "Everything in this book is a joke, therefore the advertisements are jokes." I have never come across any other case of new knowledge obtained by means of a syllogism. It must be admitted that, for a method which dominated logic for two thousand years, this contribution to the world's stock of information cannot be considered very weighty.

In the confused period that followed the Renaissance break with the logic of the schoolmen, and before Boole and others cleared the way for the development of symbolic logic, it was natural that logicians would make every conceivable attempt to reconstruct the syllogism or extend it to cover new forms of inference. Francis Bacon spoke of the syllogism as having "been beaten over and over by the subtlest labors of men's wits." Now it came in for another round of drubbing until it was almost pounded out of recognizable shape. What was needed, of course, was a broader point of view and an adequate system of symbolic notation. But until these needs were met, logicians expended an incredible amount of energy in verbal experimentation and argument. Perhaps these were necessary preliminaries to algebraic analysis, but looking back on them now they seem, especially the labors of the nineteenth century German metaphysicians, trivial and often hilarious.

Christoph von Sigwart, for instance, thought that syllogisms should be expressed in a hypothetical form: If anything is *M* it is *P;* if anything is *S* it is *M;* therefore if anything is *S* it is *P*. Franz Brentano's "existential syllogism" put all affirmative statements into a negative form: There is not a not-mortal human; there is not a not-human Socrates; therefore there is not a not-mortal Socrates. Wilhelm Schuppe decided that Aristotle was mistaken when he said that no conclusion could be derived from two negative premises. For can we not reason: No *M* is *P;* no *S* is *M;* therefore neither *S* nor *M* is *P?* And if that didn't prove the point, Schuppe had another example: No *M* is *P;* no *S* is *M;* therefore *S may* be *P*. Of course *S* may be *P* even without the premises, and in either case it may also not be *P*. Nevertheless we can say for certain that we cannot say for certain anything about the relation of *S* to *P*. Schuppe felt that this should be recognized as a kind of conclusion.

Schuppe also believed, contrary to traditional rules, that a conclusion could be obtained from two particular premises. Thus: Some *M* is *P;* some *S* is *M;* therefore some *S* may be *P*. Another Schuppe syllogism, much discussed by European logicians in his day, ran: All *P* is *M;* all *S* is *M;* therefore *S* is in some respect similar to *P*. What Schuppe meant was that *S* and *P* have in common the fact that both of them have certain attributes of *M*. If all dimes are round and all wheels are round, then wheels and dimes are similar in their roundness. One would have thought that only the German philosophers would be impressed by this discovery; nevertheless in England the great Bosanquet thought highly of it.

The most famous of these endless attempts to reshape or enlarge the Aristotelian syllogism was the "quantification of the predicate" by the Scottish philosopher Sir William Hamilton (1788–1856). Hamilton correctly perceived, as Leibnitz and many others had before him, that the predicate term in each of Aristotle's four basic assertions (A,E,I,O) is ambiguous in the sense that it does not tell us whether we are concerned with all or part of the predicate. Why not, Hamilton asked himself, increase the precision of these four statements by quantifying their predicates? In other words, for the ambiguous "All S is P" we substitute the two fully quantified assertions, "All S is *all* P" and "All S is *some* P." The old logic would treat "All men are mortal" and "All men are featherless bipeds" as identical in form; whereas in the new system we see at once that the first statement is an example of "All S is *some* P (all men are *some* mortals) and the second is an example of "All S is *all* P" (all men are *all* featherless bipeds). Since each of the four traditional statements can be replaced by two with quantified predicates, we have eight basic propositions out of which to construct syllogisms. They combine to form 512 possible moods of which 108 prove to be valid.

Let us say at once that there is no reason at all why the predicate should not be quantified. The trouble is that in doing so we are beginning to break so completely with the way in which common speech expresses class relations that, unless we develop a really complete and precise system of notation, we find ourselves forced to employ words in a clumsy and barbarous way. This was one of the criticisms of Hamilton's system voiced by his contemporary, the English mathematician Augustus De Morgan (1806–1871). De Morgan found among Hamilton's valid moods a syllogism with such cloudy phrasing that it seemed to assert that all men who were not lawyers were made of stone. De Morgan dubbed it the "Gorgon syllogism" and there was much heated British debate about it on the part of pro and anti Hamiltonians.

Hamilton attempted to remedy the obscurity of his phrasing by devising a curious system of notation that should be mentioned here because it has the superficial appearance of a diagram. Actually, there is no attempt to find a spatial analogue of classes. The system consists only of symbols with agreed-upon meanings, and rather cumbersome symbols at that in spite of Hamilton's own opinion that they were "easy, simple, compendious, all-sufficient, consistent, manifest, precise, and complete." The system employed the English C and the Greek capital gamma (each the third letter in its alphabet) for the two terms of the conclusion, and M for the middle term of the premises. The affirmative copula ("is" or "are") is a wedge-shaped line with its thick end toward the subject. It can be made negative by a vertical line crossing it at the center. A colon is used to signify a distributed (universal) term, a comma to signify an undistributed (particular) term. As an example, Figure 18 shows how Hamilton recorded the syllogism *Barbara*.

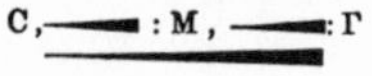

C,————: M , ————:Γ

Figure 18.

Hamilton also used his wedge-shaped marks to form triangular designs representing the three Aristotelian figures, superimposing them to produce a pattern (Figure 19) even more mysterious than

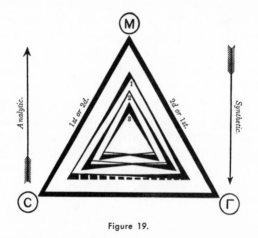

Figure 19.

Bruno's similar effort. The outside triangle, with boundary lines of even width, represents Hamilton's "unfigured syllogism." This was another of the Scottish philosopher's innovations. By transforming the phrasing of any valid syllogism with quantified predicates, he was able to express it in statements of equality. For example:

> All men and some mortals are equal.
> Socrates and some (in this case, one) men are equal.
> Socrates and some (one) mortals are equal.

Some logicians are of the opinion that this was Hamilton's only significant contribution to logic, because it suggested that logical statements might be reduced to something analogous to algebraic equations and so gave encouragement to those who were seeking a suitable algebraic notation. Unfortunately, Hamilton failed to comprehend even the most elementary mathematical concepts, and although his logical system has a neat verbal symmetry, it proved to be virtually useless in practice.[2] In common speech, for instance, if one says "Some of Picasso's paintings are mediocre," one does not *want* to quantify the predicate, it being obvious that there are other mediocre things that are not paintings by Picasso. It is one of the peculiar virtues of the traditional system that it is constructed from intentionally ambiguous statements such as occur in common discourse, whereas in Hamilton's system, to make a statement with an ambiguous predicate becomes an exceedingly complicated matter.

De Morgan also quantified the predicate in a system even more elaborate than Hamilton's. By allowing subject and predicate terms to have both positive and negative forms, he arrived at thirty-two basic statements, though many of them are merely different ways of saying the same thing. Hamilton accused De Morgan of plagiarism, and for many years the two men argued with each other in books and magazine articles—perhaps the bitterest and funniest debate about formal logic since the time of the schoolmen, though most of the humor as well as insight was on the side of De Morgan. They fought, De Morgan once recalled, like a cat and dog, "one dogmatical, the other categorical." De Morgan always maintained that he deliberately softened his verbal fire because of Hamilton's ill health, though at times he suspected that replying to Hamilton in the same abusive tone Hamilton employed might have given the ailing metaphysician a beneficial shot in the arm.

De Morgan's many contributions to logic, owing to his mathematical skill, proved more fruitful than Hamilton's, though not so fruitful as the work of Boole. In his *Budget of Paradoxes,* Book I, pp. 333 ff., De Morgan summarized his work under six heads, each propounding a new type of syllogism—relative, undecided, exemplar, numerical, onzymatic, and transposed. His example of a relative syllogism is: *X* is the brother of *Y; X* is not the uncle of *Z;* therefore *Z* is not the child of *Y*. An undecided syllogism: some men are not capable of tracing consequences; we cannot be sure that there are beings responsible for consequences who are incapable of tracing consequences; therefore we cannot be sure that all men are responsible for the consequences of their actions. The term "exemplar" refers, De Morgan writes, to a system he worked out for the purpose of correcting defects in Hamilton's logic, but which turned out to be the same as Aristotle's.

De Morgan's numerical syllogism is of special interest because it shows how easily traditional class logic slides over into arithmetic. He gives two examples, the first of which is: most Y's are X's; most Y's are Z's; therefore some X's are Z's. The second example presupposes that 100 Y's exist. We can now reason: 70 X's are Y's; 40 Z's are Y's; therefore at least 10 X's are Z's. Boole, Jevons, and many other pioneers of modern logic discussed syllogisms of this type at considerable length.[3] "Onzymatic" refers to De Morgan's expansion of the Aristotelian system by the use of negative terms and quantified predicates (see his *Syllabus of a Proposed System of Logic,* 1860). As an example of a transposed syllogism he cites: some X's are not Y's; for every X there is a Y which is Z; therefore some Z's are not X's.

The initial letters of the names of these six new varieties of syllogism, De Morgan points out, can be arranged to spell "Rue not!" indicating his unrepentance for having invented them. He adds, however, that followers of the old logic can take comfort from the fact that the same letters can be transposed to spell "True? No!"

All these strange forms and extensions of the syllogism so far mentioned (and they are but a fraction of the pseudo-syllogisms proposed by various logicians of the last century) are of little interest to a modern logician. They were courageous verbal attempts to extend the domain of formal logic beyond its traditional boundaries, but from the standpoint of modern symbolic logic they appear obvious and uninteresting. Some are merely new verbal ways of making an old assertion, like saying that 8 minus 3 equals 5 instead of saying 5 plus 3 equals 8. Others put into a syllogistic form a type of inference quite different from that involved in an Aristotelian syllogism. Such forms may be perfectly valid but they no more constitute a criticism or reform of the traditional syllogism than the theorems of non-Euclidean geometry can be said to criticize or reform the Pythagorean theorem. We now know that Aristotle's syllogism is only one of an infinite variety of forms of inference, but within its own domain it does exactly what it is supposed to do. Leibnitz thought it was "one of the most beautiful inventions of the human spirit," and there is no reason why a logician today need disagree, even though he finds the syllogism's structure no longer a field for further exploration.

It was of course the development of an adequate symbolic notation that reduced the syllogism to triviality and rendered obsolete all the quasi-syllogisms that had been so painfully and exhaustively analyzed by the nineteenth century logicians. At the same time, many a controversy that once seemed important no longer seemed so. Few logicians care today whether a syllogism is or is not reduced to the first figure, or whether we should recognize three figures or four. Perhaps one reason why these old issues faded so quickly was that, shortly after Boole laid the foundations for an algebraic notation, John Venn came forth with an ingenious improvement on Euler's circles. The result was a diagrammatic method so perfectly isomorphic with the Boolean class algebra, and picturing the structure of class logic with such visual clarity, that even a nonmathematically minded philosopher could "see" what the new logic was all about.

To understand exactly how Venn's method works, let us apply it first to a syllogism. We begin by drawing three circles that intersect like the trade-mark of Ballantine's ale (Figure 20). The circles are labeled S (subject), M (middle term), and P (predicate). All the points inside circle S are regarded as members of class S. All points outside the same circle are regarded as not-S. (In this book we shall adopt the convention of symbolizing a negation by placing a $\sim$ before the term: $\sim S$.) The same applies to the other circles. As we see by inspection, the circles overlap in such a way that, if we label each compartment with appropriate letters to indicate its members, we shall have a compartment for every possible three-term combination of the three letters and their negations (Figure 21). The region outside all three circles will represent the region of $\sim S \sim M \sim P$, or all those things that are not members of any of the three classes singled out for consideration.

The following conventions must be adopted. If we wish to show that a compartment is empty (has no members) we shade it. If we wish to show that it has members, we place a small X inside it. If we do not know whether an X belongs in one compartment or an adjacent one, we put it on the border between the two areas.

Let us now diagram the premise "All S is M." We interpret this to mean that the class of things which are S and $\sim M$ is empty;

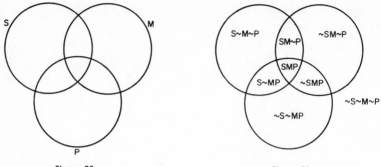

Figure 20.   Figure 21.

therefore we shade all compartments in which we find these two terms (Figure 22).

Our second premise, let us say, is "No *M* is *P*." This clearly asserts that all compartments containing the combination *MP* are empty. So we shade the diagram further, as shown in Figure 23.

At this point we must inspect the circles to see if we can draw a valid conclusion concerning the relation of *S* to *P*. We can. All areas containing both *S* and *P* are empty; hence we conclude "No *S* is *P*." If we assume that *S* is not an empty class, we may also conclude (since only one compartment in *S* is not shaded) that "Some *S* is not *P*." (This is called a "weak" conclusion because it may be derived by immediate inference from a universal or "stronger" conclusion, "No *S* is *P*.")

One more illustration is needed to make clear how particular premises are handled. "Some *S* is *M*" requires an *X* on the border of the *P* circle as shown in Figure 24, because we do not know which of the two compartments (or perhaps both) may have members. If our next premise is "All *M* is *P*" it will eliminate one of these compartments, allowing us to shift the *X* to the non-empty area as shown in Figure 25. Inspection now reveals that from the two premises we may validly conclude that "Some *S* is *P*."

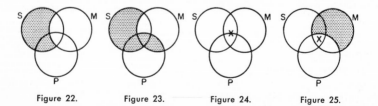

Figure 22.   Figure 23.   Figure 24.   Figure 25.

What we have been doing, in a sense, is to translate the verbal symbols of a syllogism into a problem of topology. Each circle is a closed curve, and according to the "Jordan theorem" of topology a closed curve must divide all points on the plane into those which are inside and those which are outside the curve. The points inside each circle constitute a distinct "set" or "class" of points. We thus have a simple geometrical model by means of which we can show exactly which points lie within or without a given set. The question now arises, do the topological laws involved here underlie the logic of class inclusion, or do the laws of class inclusion underlie the topological laws? It is clearly a verbal question. Neither underlies the other. We have in the Venn circles and in the syntax of a syllogism two different ways of symbolizing the same structure— one grammatical, the other geometrical. Neither, as Peirce expresses it, is "the cause or principle of the other."

A word or two now about how the circles may be used for showing class propositions linked by a disjunctive ("or") relation. Suppose we wish to say that all X is either Y or Z, taking "or" in

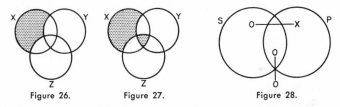

Figure 26.   Figure 27.   Figure 28.

the inclusive sense of "either or both." Figure 26 shows how simply this is done. To change this to an "exclusive" disjunction ("either but not both") we have only to shade the central area as shown in Figure 27. More complex disjunctive statements, jointly asserted, require other stratagems. Peirce suggested (*Collected Papers,* Vol. 4, pp. 307ff.) a simple way that this could be done. It involves the use of X's and O's to stand for presence or absence of members, then connecting them by a line to indicate disjunction. For example, Figure 28 shows how Peirce diagramed the statement "Either all S is P or some P is not-S, and either no S is P or no not-S is not-P."

Hypothetical class statements such as "If all A is B then all B is C," and other types of compound statements, do not readily admit of diagraming. The best procedure seems to be, following another suggestion of Peirce's (*op. cit.*, p. 315), to draw Venn diagrams of Venn diagrams. We shall see how this is done when we consider, later in the chapter, the use of the Venn circles for depicting truth-value statements in the propositional calculus.

It is interesting to note that, by changing at least one of the circles to a rectangle, the Venn diagram easily takes care of numerical syllogisms in which terms are quantified by "most" or by numbers. Figure 29 shows how one can diagram the syllogism: there are ten

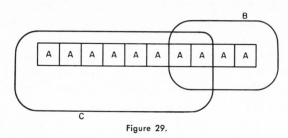

Figure 29.

A's of which four are *B*'s; eight *A*'s are *C*'s; therefore at least two *B*'s are *C*'s. Some elementary problems of probability also lend themselves to this type of diagram. Peirce suggested a different method of using circles for problems involving numerically quantified classes (*op. cit.*, p. 315), but his proposal is more notational than diagrammatic.

One of the merits of the Venn system is that it can be extended in principle to take care of any number of terms. The simplest way to provide for four terms is to use ellipses as shown in Figure 30 (it being impossible to make four circles intersect on a plane in the desired manner). The following problem, taken from Venn's *Symbolic Logic,* will suffice to indicate the scope and power of the method.

> Every *Y* is either *X* and not *Z,* or *Z* and not *X.*
> Every *WY* is either both *X* and *Z* or neither of the two.
> All *XY* is either *W* or *Z,* and all *YZ* is either *X* or *W.*

If we diagram these statements properly, as shown in Figure 31, we see at once the surprising conclusion. The premises make it impossible for any *Y* to exist.

As the number of terms increases, the diagram of course becomes more involved. It is possible to draw any number of closed curves that intersect in the necessary manner, but beyond four it is difficult to devise diagrams that permit the eye to grasp quickly the spots that are inside or outside a given curve. The more terms involved, the more peculiar become the shapes of the curves.[4] For five terms, Venn proposed the diagram shown in Figure 32. This has, however, the defect of giving class Z the shape of a doughnut, the small ellipse in the center being *outside* Z but inside W and Y. Beyond five terms, Venn thought it best to abandon hope of keep-

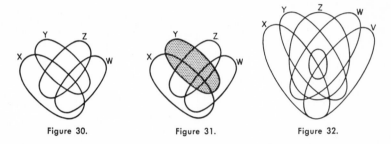

Figure 30.   Figure 31.   Figure 32.

ing all parts of one class within a closed curve, and simply to divide a rectangle into the desired number of subcompartments, labeling each with a different combination of the terms.

The first published suggestion for a rectangular graph of this sort was an article titled "A Logical Diagram for n Terms," by Allan Marquand, then a fellow at Johns Hopkins University. It appeared in the *Philosophical Magazine,* Vol. 12, October, 1881, p. 266. As we shall see in Chapter 6, Marquand also made use of this graph in the construction of his logic machine. Figure 33 pictures a Marquand graph for six terms. The square marked X indicates the class $\sim AB \sim C \sim DEF$. By shading areas asserted empty, and marking with an X the areas known to have members, problems involving six terms can be solved in the same manner as with Venn circles. This type of graph, like Lambert's system of linear diagraming, lies on the border line between a highly iconic system such as Venn's, and a noniconic system of notation. It reminds us that there is no sharp line separating symbolic notation from a diagram. Even algebraic notation is in some degree iconic, if only in the fact that single symbols stand for single terms, and even the most iconic diagram must make use of some conventions of a noniconic nature.

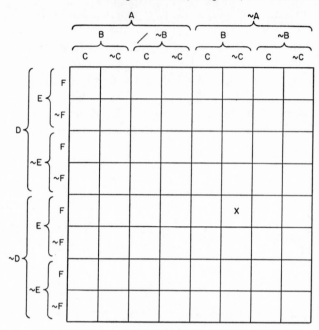

Figure 33.

Other types of graphs capable of extension to *n* terms have been proposed. Alexander Macfarlane, a professor of physics at the University of Texas, abandoned the square graph for a long narrow strip subdivided as shown in Figure 34. Macfarlane called this a "logical spectrum." Null classes are indicated by gray shading. Compartments excluded by the premises are shaded black.

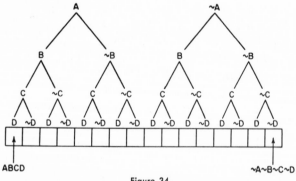

Figure 34.

Indeterminate classes are indicated by shading half the compartment black. The system was first explained in an article titled "The Logical Spectrum," *Philosophical Magazine*, Vol. 19, 1885, p. 286. In the *Proceedings of the American Association for the Advancement of Science,* Vol. 39, 1890, p. 57, in a paper titled "Adaptation of the Method of the Logical Spectrum to Boole's Problem," Macfarlane showed how easily his diagram solved an involved problem posed by Boole on p. 146 of his *Laws of Thought*.

A method of dividing a square, somewhat different from Marquand's, was proposed by William J. Newlin, of Amherst College, in an article titled "A New Logical Diagram," *Journal of Philosophy, Psychology, and Scientific Methods,* Vol. 3, Sept. 13, 1906, p. 539. Still another rectangular method was suggested by the distinguished Harvard philosopher William E. Hocking in one of his rare moments of concern with formal logic. Hocking's paper, "Two Extensions of the Use of Graphs in Elementary Logic," appeared in the *University of California Publications in Philosophy,* Vol. 2, No. 2, 1909, p. 31.

Another interesting Marquand-type graph, using colored counters to indicate presence or absence of class members, was invented by Lewis Carroll and first explained in his delightfully written little book, *The Game of Logic,* 1886. The game, Carroll tells us in his preface, requires one player *at least.* Purchasers of the book also received an envelope containing a card with Carroll's diagram, to be used as a board for the game, and nine cardboard counters (four red and five gray). This card is reproduced in Figure 35.

The large square on the card is so divided that its areas represent all three-term combinations of X, Y, M and their negations (Carroll adopts the convention of using an apostrophe to indicate negation). The upper half of this square is $X;$ the lower half is X' (not-X). The left side of the square is Y, the right side Y'. M (the middle term, for Carroll is here concerned only with the syllogism) is indicated by the space inside the interior square. M' is the area between this inner square and the outer border of the diagram.

To diagram the premises of a syllogism we simply mark the appropriate compartments with counters—a red counter for spaces known to contain members, a gray counter for spaces known to be empty. If we know that at least one of two adjacent compartments has members, but are not sure which one, the red counter is placed on the border between the two areas. After we have suitably marked the graph in accord with our premises, inspection of the diagram will give us the conclusion, if any, that we may reach

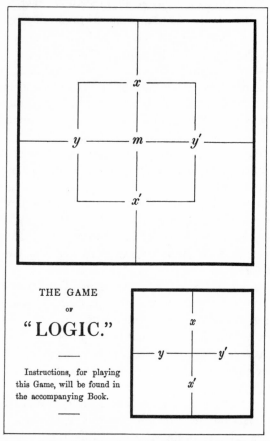

Figure 35. Reproduction of the board used in playing Lewis Carroll's logic game.

concerning the relation of X to Y. The smaller square in the lower right corner of the card is used merely for recording the conclusion.

Carroll's diagram, like that of Venn and the various extensions of Venn's method, easily takes care of syllogisms with mixtures of positive and negative forms of the same term. In traditional logic such statements would have to be rephrased to arrive at a valid syllogistic form. For example, consider the following typically Carrollian problem:

> All teetotalers like sugar.
> No nightingale drinks wine.

If we substitute letters for the terms we have:

> All *M* are *X*
> No *Y* is not-*M*

By placing the counters according to Carroll's conventions, we quickly discover that we may draw the valid conclusion "No *Y* is not-*X*" or "No nightingale dislikes sugar." Carroll himself points out that traditional logicians would not admit this to be a valid syllogism (although as we have seen, De Morgan and others included such forms in their expansions of the traditional logic). "They have a sort of nervous dread," Carroll writes, "of Attributes beginning with a negative particle. . . . And thus, having (from sheer nervousness) excluded a quantity of very useful forms, they have made rules which, though quite applicable to the few forms which they allow of, are of no use at all when you consider all possible forms."

"Let us not quarrel with them, dear Reader!" Carroll continues. "There is room enough in the world for both of us. Let us quietly take our broader system: and, if they choose to shut their eyes to all these useful forms, and to say 'They are not Syllogisms at all!' we can but stand aside, and let them Rush upon their Fate!"

In a later book, *Symbolic Logic,* 1896 (reissued in 1955 by Dover Publications and Berkeley Enterprises), Carroll explained his diagrammatic method in greater detail, distinguishing it from the systems of Euler and Venn in the following characteristic manner:

> My Method of Diagrams *resembles* Mr. Venn's, in having separate Compartments assigned to the various Classes, and in marking these Compartments as *occupied* or as *empty;* but it *differs* from his Method, in assigning a *closed* area to the *Universe of Discourse,* so that the Class which, under Mr. Venn's liberal sway, has been ranging at will through Infinite Space, is suddenly dismayed to find itself "cabin'd, cribb'd, confined," in a limited Cell like any other Class!

Apparently Carroll was not familiar with Marquand's earlier proposed diagram, because it likewise assigns a closed area to the region outside of the classes under consideration. Carroll's graph, also like Marquand's, can be extended to *n* terms. *Symbolic Logic* pictures a number of these extensions, including a 256-cell graph for eight terms. The frontispiece of this book, reproduced in Figure

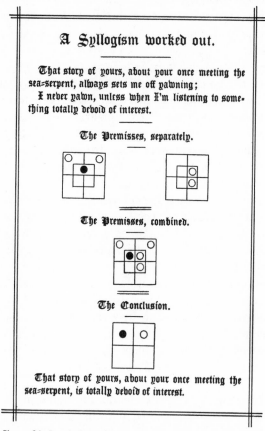

Figure 36. Frontispiece of Lewis Carroll's *Symbolic Logic*, 1886.

36, shows how the counters are placed to solve a syllogism about a sea-serpent story that induces yawning.

All the foregoing methods of diagraming class-inclusion logic were developed before the modern truth-value propositional calculus assumed its present form and importance. As we have seen, the terms of class logic stand for classes. In the propositional calculus, terms stand for statements (such as "It is raining") which may be regarded as true or false, and which are logically related by such "connectives" as "and," "or," "not," "both," "if . . . then." The question naturally arises, can these diagrams be used for solving problems in the propositional calculus? The answer is yes, as Venn himself recognized though he did not elaborate the technique. In fact, if the premises are not complicated by compound (parenthetical) assertions, the Venn diagrams can be used with surprising efficiency.

The propositional calculus first arose, it is worth recalling, as an interpretation of the class calculus. The correspondence between the two calculi is so close that every class statement has a corresponding propositional form. For example, "All A is B" can be interpreted to mean, "If X is a member of class A, then X is a member of class B." Similarly, "If A is true then B is true" may be interpreted to mean, "The class of all occasions on which A is true is included in the class of occasions on which B is true." "If it rains, I stay indoors," is a truth-value assertion. But if I say the same thing differently, "All rainy days are days when I stay indoors," it becomes a class statement. Every statement in truth-function logic has a similar class analogue. As the diagraming of these statements will make clear, they are simply different verbal ways of stating the same underlying logical structure.

To use the Venn circles for propositional logic we must first interpret them in a different way. Each circle now stands for a proposition which may be either true or false, rather than a class which may or may not have members. The labels on the various compartments (Figure 37) indicate possible or impossible combinations of true and false values of the respective terms. Just as we formerly shaded a compartment to show that it had no members, we now shade it to indicate that it is an impossible combination of truth values. Conversely, an unshaded compartment indicates a permissible combination. (Note in Figure 37 that the combination $\sim A \sim B \sim C$ is shown as a small circle outside the other three. This is done to simplify the shading, when necessary, of this area.)

If we wish to show that A is true, we shade all compartments containing $\sim A$ (Figure 38). To show that A is false, we shade all areas containing A (Figure 39).

A and $\sim A$ are of course negations of each other. Their diagrams are like positive and negative prints; to change from one to the other we have only to exchange black and white areas. This is one of the delightful features of the method. The diagram of any truth-value assertion can be converted to its negation by following this simple procedure.

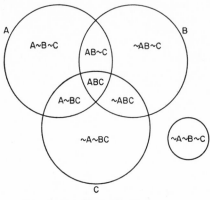

Figure 37.

Let us see how we go about depicting a statement of implication, "If *A* is true, then *B* is true" (symbolized as $A \supset B$). A truth table for this relation tells us there are four possible true and false combinations (*TT, TF, FT,* and *FF*) of which only the combination *TF* is invalid. Hence we eliminate all compartments containing $A \sim B$. The result (shown in Figure 40) is, as we would expect, a diagram identical with the diagram for the class statement, "All *A* is *B*."

The nature of "material implication" is easily explained by this figure. If we add to it the statement that *A* is false (by shading all unshaded areas containing *A*) it will appear as in Figure 39. The white areas in this diagram tell us that *B* may be either true or false. In other words, a false proposition "implies" any proposition, true or false. On the other hand, if we make *A* true (Figure

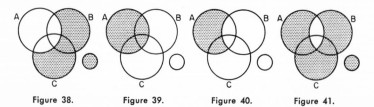

Figure 38.   Figure 39.   Figure 40.   Figure 41.

41), we see immediately that B must be true. Any true proposition, therefore, implies any other true one.

Figure 42 introduces the notational symbols that will be used throughout this book for all binary (two-term) truth-value relations for which there are commonly used symbols. The diagram for each relation is shown on the left. On the right is the "negative" diagram for the negation of each relation.

To apply these diagrams to relations between B and C, we have only to rotate the page until the A and B circles correspond to the positions of the B and C circles. In the same way we can turn the page to bring the A and B circles to the positions of C and A. After we work with the diagrams for a while, the patterns are soon memorized and problems involving no more than three terms can be solved with great speed. After a time, elementary problems of this sort can even be solved in the head. One has only to form a mental picture of the circles, then perform on them the necessary shadings. Both Venn and Carroll, incidentally, wrote of the ease with which they learned to solve logic problems mentally by their respective methods, just as an expert abacus operator can move the beads in a mental image of an abacus, or a chess master can play a game of chess blindfolded. Using the circles mentally is, of course, much easier than blindfold chess or abacus operation.

Tautologous or equivalent statements are rendered visually obvious by the circles. For example, we make separate diagrams for the following two assertions:

$$A \lor \sim B$$
$$B \supset A$$

The two diagrams prove to be identical.

Let us now consider a simple three-term problem involving the following premises:

$$A \supset B \quad (A \text{ implies } B)$$
$$B \not\equiv C \quad (\text{Either } B \text{ or } C \text{ but not both})$$
$$A \lor C \quad (\text{Either } A \text{ or } C \text{ or both})$$
$$C \supset A \quad (C \text{ implies } A)$$

After shading the circles for the above assertions we are left with the diagram shown in Figure 43. Only one compartment, $AB \sim C$,

- ▪ Conjunction ("And")
- ⊃ Implication ("If ___ then ___")
- ∨ Disjunction, alternation ("Either ___ or ___ or both")
- ≢ Exclusive disjunction, non-equivalence ("Either ___ or ___ but not both"
- ≡ Equivalence ("If and only if ___ then ___")
- | Non-conjunction ("Not both ___ and ___")
- ~ Negation ("Not")

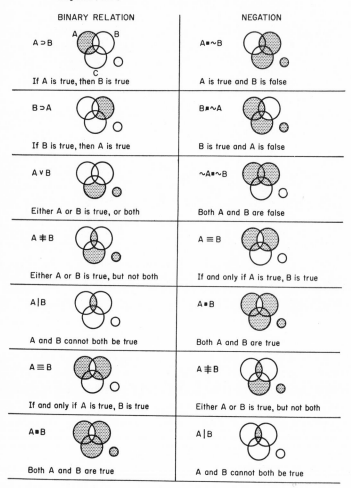

BINARY RELATION	NEGATION
A ⊃ B	A ▪ ~B
If A is true, then B is true	A is true and B is false
B ⊃ A	B ▪ ~A
If B is true, then A is true	B is true and A is false
A ∨ B	~A ▪ ~B
Either A or B is true, or both	Both A and B are false
A ≢ B	A ≡ B
Either A or B is true, but not both	If and only if A is true, B is true
A	B	A ▪ B
A and B cannot both be true	Both A and B are true
A ≡ B	A ≢ B
If and only if A is true, B is true	Either A or B is true, but not both
A ▪ B	A	B
Both A and B are true	A and B cannot both be true

Figure 42.

has not been eliminated. We are forced to conclude, therefore, that, on the basis of the logical structure asserted by the four premises, *A* and *B* must be true and *C* false.

Four-term problems can be solved in the same manner on Venn's four-term figure of intersecting ellipses. Problems with larger numbers of variables are best handled on graphs such as those suggested by Marquand, Carroll, and others, or else one can simply make a list of all the combinations, then cross out the invalid ones. (As we shall see in Chapter 5, this was the method used by Jevons, but of course it is not a diagrammatic one.) After we have

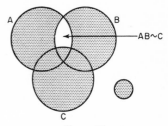

Figure 43.

eliminated all the invalid combinations, an inspection of the remaining ones will give us all that can be validly inferred from the premises. If, for instance, we find that term *D* is true in all the remaining compartments, then *D* must be true. If we find permissible combinations containing both *D* and ~*D*, we know that *D* is undecided by the premises and may be either true or false. If in performing our eliminations we discover that *all* compartments become shaded, we know that the last diagramed statement introduces a logical contradiction, leading to an absurdity in which nothing can be said about any of the terms. In view of the obvious classroom value of this method of diagraming truth-value problems, it is surprising that most logic textbooks confine their discussion of Venn circles entirely to class logic and the syllogism.

A few remarks should be made about diagraming compound statements with parentheses, such as: $(A \lor B) \supset (B \lor C)$. This asserts that if the relation "$A \lor B$" is a true relation then the relation "$B \lor C$" must also be true.

How can this be shown on the Venn circles? We can of course expand the statement by algebraic methods into a longer statement without parentheses, then make our diagram; but if we do this, we might as well proceed to use algebraic methods throughout. On the other hand, there seems to be no simple way in which the statement, as it stands, can be diagramed. The best procedure is probably to follow the suggestion Peirce made for handling parenthetical statements in class logic—to make separate Venn diagrams for

the two relations inside of parentheses, then connect them with another Venn diagram shaded to represent implication.

Figure 44 shows how this appears. The lower set of circles expresses the relation of implication between the binary relations

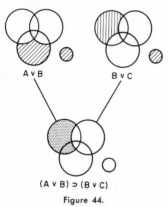

A ∨ B

B ∨ C

(A ∨ B) ⊃ (B ∨ C)

Figure 44.

expressed by the other two sets. This
lower set is shaded black because we
know the relation to be valid. Gray
is used for the other sets of circles
because we have no way of knowing
whether the relation each expresses
is valid or not. If in the course of
diagraming other premises we discover that, say, the relation expressed
by the upper left circles, "*A* ∨ *B*," is
valid, we can then blacken the gray
area. If, however, we discover that
this relation is false, we must con-
vert the relation to its negation. As we have shown earlier, this
is done by blacking the white areas and erasing the shading in the
other areas.

A knowledge of the truth values of *A* and *B*, and in some cases
a knowledge of the truth value of one term only, is sufficient to tell
us whether the relation *A* ∨ *B* is true or false. If, for example, we
learn that both terms are false, this clearly contradicts the relation
and so we must change it to its negation. If we learn that *A* is true,
this is all we need to know to be sure that the binary relation *A* ∨ *B*
is true, for it will be true regardless of whether *B* is true or false.
The reader who desires to pursue this further will not find it difficult
to work out rules for handling any type of compound statement,
including statements that are mixtures of class and propositional assertions. It also is possible to use closed curves and Marquand-type
graphs for diagraming certain types of multivalued logics, but if
there are more than three terms the diagram or graph becomes so
intricate that it ceases to be any sort of visual aid.

The American philosopher Charles Peirce (1839–1914), mentioned several times in this chapter, was deeply interested in logic
diagrams. In addition to his extension of Venn's method and an
early attempt at what he called an "entitative graph" (later discarded; it was "haunted," Peirce confessed, by "aniconicity"), he

finally worked out a comprehensive system by which he believed he could give geometric expression to any conceivable assertion or logical argument. Peirce called it his system of "existential graphs," the term "existential" referring to the graphs' power of depicting any existing state of any aspect of any possible universe. His first attempt to publish a description of the method was in 1897 when he sent an article on the subject to *The Monist* magazine. The editor returned it on the ground that the system could probably be improved. Peirce was so annoyed by this rejection that in a paper written six years later he went out of his way to note that he had not yet found it necessary to make any fundamental alterations in his original scheme. For the rest of his life Peirce regarded the existential graph as his most important contribution to logic; his chef-d'œuvre, he liked to call it. Some idea of how much store Peirce set by this method can be gained from the following quotation:

"Diagrammatic reasoning is the only really fertile reasoning. If logicians would only embrace this method, we should no longer see attempts to base their science on the fragile foundations of metaphysics or a psychology not based on logical theory; and there would soon be such an advance in logic that every science would feel the benefit of it." (*Collected Papers*, Vol. 4, p. 459.)

Again: ". . . if one learns to think of relations in the forms of those graphs, one gets the most distinct and esthetically as well as otherwise intellectually, iconic conception of them likely to suggest circumstances of theoretic utility, that one can obtain in any way. The aid that the system of graphs thus affords to the process of logical analysis, by virtue of its own analytical purity, is surprisingly great, and reaches further than one would dream. Taught to boys and girls before grammar, to the point of thorough familiarization, it would aid them through all their lives. For there are few important questions that the analysis of ideas does not help to answer. The theoretical value of the graphs, too, depends on this." (*Collected Papers*, Vol. 4, p. 516.)

There is not space available in this volume to give a coherent account of Peirce's fantastic diagrammatic method even if I understood it fully, and I am far from assured I do. His several papers on the topic (reprinted in Vol. 4 of his *Collected Papers*) are written in such an elliptic, involuted style that one is led to wonder if Peirce harbored unconscious compulsions toward cloudy writing that would enable him to complain later of his critics' inability to understand him. Add to this opaque style his use of scores of strange terms invented by himself and altered from time to time, and the lack of sufficient drawings to illustrate the meaning of these terms, and the task of comprehending his system becomes formidable indeed.

A few things, however, are clear. Peirce was not attempting to create a method that could be used efficiently for the solution of logic problems, although his graphs could be so used. If one would devote several hours a day for a week or two to practicing with the graphs, Peirce wrote, he would soon be able to solve problems with a facility "about equal" to that of any algebraic method yet devised, including one such system of his own. What Peirce was primarily interested in, however, was a method of analyzing in detail the structure of all deductive reasoning, including mathematical reasoning; breaking the structure into all its elements and giving each element the simplest, most iconic geometrical representation possible. In this way the mind would be able to "see" the logical structure in a fashion analogous to seeing a geographical area when you look at a map. The graphs, he wrote, "put before us moving pictures of thought." They render the structure "literally visible before one's very eyes." In doing this they free the structure from all the "puerilities about words" with which so many English logical works are strewn. "Often not merely strewn with them," he adds, "but buried so deep in them, as by a great snowstorm, as to obstruct the reader's passage and render it fatiguing in the extreme."

In addition to making for clarity, Peirce also believed that, once a formal structure had been adequately graphed, it could then be experimented upon in a manner similar to the way a scientist experiments with a structure in nature. By altering the graph in various ways, adding to it here, taking away there, and so on, one could discover new properties of the structure—properties not previously suspected. In other words, Peirce viewed his graphs in much the same way that Lull viewed his Great Art, as an instrument for the invention and discovery of new truths as well as a device for proving old ones.

Peirce's system is topological throughout. That is to say, his diagrams are unconcerned with size or shape in any metrical sense, but only with such geometrical properties as remain unaltered if the "sheet of assertion" (the piece of paper on which the graphs are drawn) were made of rubber that could be twisted and stretched (or, more precisely, given what topologists call a "continuous deformation"). For example, Peirce made abundant use of closed curves (called "cuts" or "seps") that divide the sheet of assertion into outside and inside regions. The system also relies heavily on "lines of identity," heavy unbroken lines (the shape or length being of no significance) that connect two signs, one at each end of the line. These properties of enclosure and connectivity are of course topological, and in one interesting passage (*Collected Papers*, Vol. 4, p. 346) Peirce says that he expects his system of graphs to contribute toward an understanding of topological laws. On more than one occasion he likens his graphs to chemical diagrams that show how the molecules of a given substance are bonded together in various complex topological structures. The graphs bear an even stronger resemblance, in both appearance and purpose, to the topological figures employed by Kurt Lewin in his *Principles of Topological Psychology*,[5] 1936, and by followers of Lewin who are presently laboring in the field known as "group dynamics."

Peirce sought to make his diagrams as iconic as possible, and in this he partially succeeded. For example: his use of two closed curves, one inside the other (he called this a "scroll"), to indicate what is now called material implication. The outer circle ("outloop") represents the antecedent which, if true, necessitates the truth of all that part of the graph inside the smaller circle ("inloop"). There is also, as Peirce points out, an iconic aspect to his line of identity, as well as its extension into a branching-tree device called a "ligature." But in many other respects (e.g., the use of dotted, wavy, and saw-toothed lines, the use of the underside or "verso" of the sheet as well as other layers of paper beneath to represent other dimensions of possibility, and so on) the iconic aspect is entirely or almost entirely lost. This lack of iconicity is particularly glaring, as Peirce himself confesses, in his later attempt to distinguish within his system the three traditional varieties of modality—factual truth, possible truth, and necessary truth. Peirce did this by the use of three different heraldic "tinctures"—color, fur, and metal—each in turn divided into four types. (The four "colors" are azure, gules, vert, and purpure; the four "furs" are sable, ermine, vair, and potent; the four "metals," argent, or, fer, and plomb.)

How Ramon Lull would have been intrigued and utterly mystified by these strange variegated symbols!

These noniconic aspects of Peirce's system give it an air of arbitrariness and disjointedness. The parts do not seem to hang together. One has the feeling that, if twelve competent modern logicians were to set themselves the task of constructing similar graphs that would encompass the whole of logic, each would come up with a different system, and each as good if not better than Peirce's. At any rate, there is no question that Peirce, like Ramon Lull (whom Peirce in an unguarded moment once called an "acute logician"), held a greatly exaggerated notion of the value of his diagrams. That they were an aid to his own thinking is undeniable. He obviously found it desirable to think more in pictures than in words, and after having worked for some twenty years with his own diagrams, he could probably "see" their meanings as effortlessly as an experienced orchestra leader can run his eyes over a musical score and "hear" the orchestration. For the rest of us, however, it would mean a gigantic effort of practice and study to master Peirce's intricate technique to the point of usefulness, and the consensus of logicians who have undergone this initiation is that the system is not worth this effort.[6]

We must remember, however, that Peirce undertook his Gargantuan project at a time when symbolic logic was in its infancy. In many aspects of his method he was a pioneer groping in unfamiliar realms. His logic graphs are still the most ambitious yet attempted, and they are filled with suggestive hints of what can be done along such lines. Peirce himself expected successors to take up where he left off and bring his system to perfection. It would be rash to say that no one in the future will be able to build upon it something closer to what Peirce was striving for. In the meantime, it stands as a characteristic monument to one man's extraordinary industry, brilliance, and eccentricity.

References

1. Venn's criticisms of both Euler's and Lambert's methods are reinforced by Peirce in his *Collected Papers*, Vol. 4, pp. 297 ff. Peirce wrote of course before the development of modern topology, and so his analysis of why Euler's circles do what they do has for modern ears a quaint clumsiness. For a defense and improvement of Lambert's linear method, see the chapter on logic diagrams in John Neville Keynes's *Studies and Exercises in Formal Logic*, fourth edition, 1906.

2. If the reader cares to have a clearer picture of Hamilton's system and method of notation than was possible to sketch here, he is advised to consult the chapter on Hamilton in Francis Bowen's *A Treatise on Logic,* 1864. This is a once popular college text by one of Hamilton's strongest admirers. Going directly to Hamilton's own works will probably tell the reader more about the system than he cares to know.

3. The numerical syllogism, as well as quantified predicates and the reduction of syllogisms to equations of identity, were all clearly formulated before 1800 by Charles Stanhope, inventor of the world's first logic machine. Stanhope published nothing about this in his lifetime, however; so his work could not have been known to Hamilton and De Morgan. An account of Stanhope's logic will be given in Chapter 4.

4. Edmund C. Berkeley, in his paper on "Boolean Algebra (the technique for manipulating 'and,' 'or,' 'not,' and conditions) and Applications to Insurance" (first published in *The Record* of the American Institute of Actuaries, 1937–1938, reprinted 1952 by Edmund C. Berkeley and Associates) adopts a system of forming Venn diagrams in which rectangles and curved compartments are combined. Beyond four terms the closed curves assume a horseshoe shape, but they remain continuous and there are simple rules for forming as many of them as desired.

5. In my opinion Lewin's "topological psychology," as well as his "vector psychology" and "field theory," belong among the century's many premature and pretentious attempts on the part of certain psychologists, in this case a Gestalt psychologist, to disguise themselves as mathematical physicists. The topological diagrams of Lewin and his admirers make intriguing blackboard illustrations for a classroom, but as sources of new insights they have proved remarkably sterile. The pseudo-mathematical jargon of the school makes it difficult to see that its pronouncements are often little more than clumsy restatements of the obvious.

6. Thomas A. Goudge, in his *Thought of C. S. Peirce,* 1950, pp. 119 ff., quotes Peirce's remark, "Yet the system is not intended as a plaything," then adds: "One can hardly avoid the conclusion that in the end Peirce permitted his graphs to become just such a 'plaything.' The fascination they exerted led to a steady increase in their internal complexity, without any corresponding increase in their positive results."

3: A Network Diagram for the Propositional Calculus

Venn circles and other diagrams of the shaded-compartment type can, as we have seen in the previous chapter, be used for solving problems in the propositional calculus. In many respects, however, their application to this type of logic is clumsy and lacking in what Peirce called "iconicity"—formal resemblance to the logical structure for which they are intended to be visual aids. This is understandable since these diagrammatic methods were originally devised for class logic. To use them for truth-value problems we have to think of the problems in terms of class logic before the diagram takes on an iconic aspect. Is it possible to diagram statements in the calculus of propositions in such a way that the diagrams exhibit more directly the formal structure of truth-value relations?

In 1951 I set myself the pleasant task of trying to work out such a system. After experimenting with several different approaches I finally hit upon the network method that will form the content of this chapter. It obviously is not intended as a method to compete in efficiency with algebraic or truth-table methods, but it does have, it seems to me, some merit in helping novices such as myself to visualize truth-value structure and to understand better the matrix method of analysis. In addition, it provides a handy means for checking results obtained by other methods. That it can be much improved, I have no doubt. Perhaps it will catch the fancy of some reader who will discover, in toying with the method, some way of eliminating its chief defects and rendering it more elegant.

The most annoying drawback of the Venn circles, when applied to propositional problems, is the difficulty of separating the premises from each other on the diagram so that they can be analyzed separately or altered as desired. This might be done by using sheets of transparent paper (shading each premise on a different sheet) but such a procedure is troublesome, and of course it cannot be applied to classroom blackboards. The network method to be explained here requires only paper and pencil, or chalk and blackboard, and it diagrams a series of premises in such fashion that the structure of each individual premise is visually separate from the others. This makes it possible for the eye to explore any desired portion of the structure in a way that is difficult on diagrams of the Venn type. Essentially, the method is a geometrical analogue of the truth-table or matrix method of handling propositional logic, its iconicity yielding valuable insights into the nature of matrix analysis.

Like all the geometric methods considered so far, this one also is topological, exploiting the "connectivity" properties of linear networks in such manner that the network becomes an isomorph of the logical structure being analyzed. That the propositional calculus can be translated into network theory has been widely recognized for almost two decades, playing an important role in the designing of electric circuits for giant computing machines and, as we shall see in Chapter 8, in the construction of electric logic machines. But so far as I am aware, this is the first attempt at a network analogue simple enough to be serviceable as a blackboard or paper method of solving truth-value problems.

The first step in diagraming a problem is to represent each term by two vertical, parallel lines which stand for the two possible truth values of each term. By convention, the line on the left represents "true," the line on the right "false." If there are, say, five terms involved in a given problem, the basic graph of Figure 45 is drawn.

A simple assertion that a term is true or false is indicated by a cross mark on the appropriate truth-value line, as shown in Figure 46.

Statements expressing a relation between two terms are shown on the graph by one, two, or three horizontal lines that connect a truth-value line of one term with a truth-value line of another.

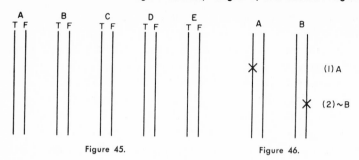

Figure 45.   Figure 46.

These horizontal lines will be called "shuttles." It is necessary to give them some sort of name, and this seems appropriate because in solving a problem, as we shall see, we actually do shuttle back and forth along these lines in much the same manner that Manhattan's 42nd Street shuttle train moves back and forth between the Seventh Avenue and Lexington Avenue subway lines.

It is apparent that only four different kinds of shuttles can be drawn to connect a given pair of terms (Figure 47).

These four shuttles correspond to the four rows of a truth table for two terms. They connect true with true, true with false, false with true, and false with false. If we now wish to show a functional relation between two terms, we have only to eliminate the shuttle or shuttles that represent invalid combinations of truth values. Or put another way, to show only shuttles that indicate permissible combinations.

To illustrate, let us consider first the relation of conjunction ("and"), symbolized by ∎. Only one line of a truth table is valid for this relation; therefore we graph it with a single shuttle, as Figure 48 makes clear.

If the relation of conjunction stands alone as a complete premise (that is, if it is not part of a longer statement), then it states unequivocally the truth value of each term. In such cases we im-

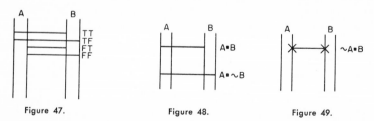

Figure 47.   Figure 48.   Figure 49.

mediately place a cross at each end of the shuttle as shown in Figure 49.

If, however, the conjunction is part of a compound statement, we cannot add the crosses for we have no way of knowing whether the relation itself is true or false. This will be made clear later when we consider the diagraming of compound statements.

The biconditional, or statement of equivalence (symbolized by ≡), requires two shuttles. In ordinary speech this is expressed by saying, "If and only if A is true, then B is true." Its truth table has two valid lines, TT and $FF;$ therefore we diagram it as in Figure 50.

The two shuttles show clearly that, if we are "riding" (to labor the subway metaphor a moment) on A's T line, we have only one shuttle that will carry us to $B,$ and it will land us on B's T line. Similarly, the only available shuttle on A's F line carries us to B's F line. The same relations hold if we move backward from B to A. In other words, if either term is true the other must be true; if either is false, the other must be false.

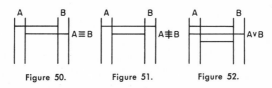

Figure 50.   Figure 51.   Figure 52.

The exclusive "or" of nonequivalence (symbolized by ≢) likewise is expressed by two shuttles (Figure 51).

The diagram shows at a glance that if one term is true the other must be false, and vice versa. A comparison of this pattern with the previous one reveals an interesting fact. Each diagram is made up of the shuttles *missing* from the other. This tells us that one is the negation of the other. Just as we transformed a Venn diagram of a binary relation into its negation by exchanging the black and white areas, so we can in this method effect the same transformation simply by erasing whatever shuttles are present and substituting those that are absent.

The inclusive "or" of disjunction ("either or both"), symbolized by v, requires three shuttles. Inspection of Figure 52 will show that it is the negation of $\sim A \;\blacksquare\; \sim B$.

The statement "not both A and B are true" (sometimes referred to as the Sheffer stroke function), will be symbolized by $A \mid B$.

It is the negation of $A \cdot B$, and likewise requires three shuttles (Figure 53).

The "If . . . then" of a conditional statement, symbolized by $\supset$, also calls for three shuttles.[1] Unlike the previous relations, it is not symmetrical. That is, the diagram has two forms, depending on which term implies the other. These two forms are indicated in Figure 54.

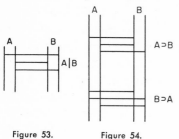

Figure 53.   Figure 54.

The shuttles reveal immediately that $A \supset B$ is the negation of $A \cdot \sim B$, and $B \supset A$ is the negation of $\sim A \cdot B$. The diagrams are excellent classroom devices for explaining the so-called paradoxes of material implication. The statement *"A implies B"* has no meaning in the propositional calculus other than what is indicated by the shuttles in its diagram; namely, that all combinations of truth values are permitted except $A \cdot \sim B$. Hence, if we let A and B stand for any two propositions whatever, we see that any true proposition (A) can only imply another true proposition (B) because only one shuttle leads from A's T line. On the other hand, two shuttles lead from A's F line, showing that any false proposition ($\sim A$) may imply any proposition, true or false (B or $\sim B$). Similarly, the two shuttles leading from B's T line tell us that any true proposition (B) may be implied by any proposition, true or false (A or $\sim A$), whereas the single shuttle terminating on B's F line indicates that a false proposition ($\sim B$) can be implied only by another false proposition ($\sim A$). The paradoxical character of such assertions as, "If grass is red then Shakespeare wrote *Hamlet*," vanishes as soon as we realize that the "if . . . then" of material implication has a different meaning in the calculus than in common speech. It is not intended to assert any causal connection between the two propositions, but only to tell us what combinations of true and false values are permitted by the relation.

We have now covered all the binary functions for which there are common expressions in the language and commonly used symbols in logic. It should be clear that any statement of a truth-value relation between two terms can easily be diagramed. The relations discussed occur so often, however, that one's use of the graph will be greatly facilitated if they are committed to memory so that it will not be necessary to pause and analyze the relation, or to refer to a chart of their shuttle patterns each time a relation has to be graphed. The order in which the shuttles for a given relation are drawn is not, of course, significant. But if they are memorized as patterns, it will be convenient to adopt a specific order of shuttles for each relation. The order adopted here is one that conforms to the most commonly used order of combinations in truth-table lines.

When one or both terms of a binary relation are negative, as, for example, $\sim A \vee B$, how do we go about drawing the required shuttles? The procedure is simple. We consider the pattern for $A \vee B$, then exchange the terminal points of A's two truth-value lines. In other words, all shuttles on A's T line are shifted to the F line; all shuttles on A's F line are shifted to the T line. The terminal points on B remain unchanged. After we have done this we shall discover that the resulting diagram is identical with the diagram for $A \supset B$. The same pattern also results if we diagram $\sim B \supset \sim A$ (in this case we must of course exchange the terminal points on the truth-value lines of *both* terms). Whenever the diagrams for two assertions are identical, then they are said to be "tautologies," that is, merely two ways of saying the same thing. We can express the identity of $\sim A \vee B$ and $A \supset B$ by connecting them with the symbol of equivalence: $\sim A \vee B \equiv A \supset B$. Such a statement is called an "equivalence formula." Diagrammatically, the equivalence of two binary relations is revealed by the fact that they have identical shuttle patterns.

Additional examples will make this clear. De Morgan called attention to two interesting tautologies known as "De Morgan's laws." One tells us that the denial of a conjunction can be expressed by denying each term separately in a disjunctive relation. Symbolically, this is the equivalence formula, $A \mid B \equiv \sim A \vee \sim B$. The other law tells us that the denial of a disjunction can be expressed by denying both terms of a conjunctive relation: $\sim(A \vee B) \equiv \sim A \blacksquare \sim B$. We can establish both laws simply by diagraming the two sides of their formula. If the diagrams are identical, then the two statements are tautological.

Before going into the matter of diagraming chains of terms connected by the same relation, or compound statements involving parentheses, let us consider the actual graphing and solution of two simple problems.

For our first problem, we are given the following four premises:

1. If A is true then B is true. $(A \supset B)$
2. Either B is true or C is true, but not both. $(B \not\equiv C)$
3. Either A is true or C is true, or both. $(A \lor C)$
4. B is true. (B)

What can we infer about A and C?

Our first step is to diagram the premises. When this is done, our graph will appear as shown in Figure 55.

The next step is to examine the network structure to see if it will unequivocally determine the truth values of A and C. Since we know the value of B, we begin our exploration at the cross mark on B's T line. We run our eyes upward along this line to see if we encounter a premise in which there is a *single* shuttle terminating on the line. In this case we find such a shuttle in premise 2. Since this shuttle indicates a permissible line of travel, and since the premise does not offer us a choice of more than one shuttle, we are obliged to follow the single shuttle to its terminal point on C's F line. Our passage on this shuttle is indicated by placing cross marks at the two terminal points of the shuttle. The cross mark on C's F line tells us that premise 2, in combination with premise 4, forces us to conclude that C is false. We next inspect C's F line and we quickly discover that in premise 3 we come upon a single shuttle terminating on this line. We make a cross mark at this point, follow the shuttle to A's T line, and make a cross mark there also.

We have now determined that C is false and A is true, but we must continue our examination of the network to make certain that the premises do not contain a contradiction. Inspection of A's T line reveals a single shuttle in premise 1. We mark the terminal point with a cross, follow the shuttle to B's T line, and mark its terminal point there. This last cross mark is consistent with our previous knowledge that B is true. Since there are no other single shuttles terminating on the truth-value lines that bear cross marks, we conclude that the premises are consistent, and consistent only with the truth of A and B, and falsity of C. If the premises had contained a contradiction, it would have forced us, in our exploration

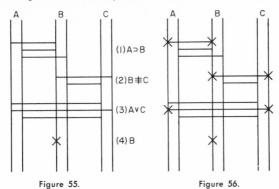

Figure 55.   Figure 56.

of the structure, to affirm both the truth and falsity of at least one term, and possibly all terms.

Figure 56 shows how the graph appears after our problem has been solved.

Let us now consider a slightly more difficult problem—one in which we are not told the truth value of any term. Our premises are:

1. In August I either wear a hat or go bareheaded.
2. I never go bareheaded in August when I have on a bow tie.
3. In August I either wear a hat or a bow tie and sometimes both.

To put these statements into symbolic form, we assign the following meanings to A, B, and C.

> A—I wear a hat in August.
> B—I wear a bow tie in August.
> C—I go bareheaded in August.

The premises can now be stated symbolically as:

1. $A \equiv C$
2. $B \mid C$
3. $A \vee B$

A network diagram of the premises will show the structure of Figure 57.

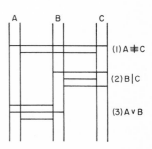

Figure 57.

We must now test this structure to see what we can discover about the truth values of its terms. We may begin anywhere; so suppose we start by making a cross on A's T line. The single shuttle in the first premise forces us to conclude that C is false, but this is as far as our exploration will take us. We can learn nothing about B.

The next step is to erase all cross marks and place a cross on A's F line. This quickly leads us to contradictions. If we explore the structure fully we find ourselves affirming the truth and falsity of all three terms.

We must conclude, therefore, that A is true and C false. One final step remains. B must be tested for both true and false values to see if contradictions arise. No such contradictions are encountered, telling us that the truth of A and the falsity of C are consistent with either value for B. Hence the answer to our problem is that in August I always wear a hat, never go bareheaded, but may or may not sport a bow tie.

In some cases the test of one term is sufficient to establish the truth values of all terms. In other problems, as in the foregoing, a test of one term will give values for only a portion of the remaining terms. Further tests then have to be made to see if the undetermined terms are capable of determination by the structure, or whether the structure leaves a certain number of terms undecidable. It may be, of course, that a given structure will leave all terms undecidable. Or it may be that certain premises are contradictory. In any case, the graph gives a clear visual picture of the structure that is open for inspection and experimentation in a way that is often difficult and confusing if one is using truth-table procedures. For example, if we have a structure that does not determine the truth value of any term, we may wish to answer such a question as, "Does the structure permit A and F to be true when D and G are false?" We have only to make these four assertions on the graph, then explore the structure to see if they lead to contradictions. It should be clear that, regardless of how many terms are involved, or how many binary relations are given, we can graph the structure and perform upon it any of the operations that are possible algebraically.

Compound statements involving parentheses can be diagramed by a simple extension of the graph. We shall illustrate this by considering the assertion $(A \vee B) \supset (C \vee D)$. The two disjunctive statements inside parentheses are first diagramed in the usual manner, as if they were two premises, except that dotted lines are used for shuttles instead of solid lines. (This corresponds to the use of gray shading when Venn circles are used for compound statements.) The dotted lines indicate the tentative nature of the shuttles; that is, we do not as yet know whether the relation they symbolize is a true or false one. If we later learn that it is true, we change the dotted lines to solid. If we learn that it is false, we leave the dotted lines (or erase them if we wish) and add in solid lines the *negation* of the original pattern. As explained earlier, this is done by supplying in solid lines the shuttles *missing* from the dotted pattern. In either case, if the final result is a *single* shuttle, we immediately place crosses on its terminal points to affirm the truth-value lines that are involved.

The two parenthetical statements must now be connected on the graph by a relation of implication. To do this, we adopt the following procedure. At the right of the graph we draw two pairs of *horizontal* truth-value lines, each pair opposite one of the statements already graphed. By convention we assume the lower line of each pair to be true, the upper line false. If we give the paper a quarter turn clockwise, these truth-value lines will appear as a familiar graph for two terms, except in this case each term is itself a binary relation. On this graph we place the shuttle lines of implication to show that one relation implies the other. These shuttles are solid lines since there is no uncertainty about their validity. The entire graph will now appear like Figure 58.

If a single term is involved in a compound statement, for example, $A \vee (B \bullet C)$, the same procedure is adopted. In such a case we show the tentative character of A by using a half cross or diagonal mark. It is easily changed to true by adding the other half, or negated by placing a cross mark on A's F line. The graph for the entire expression will appear as in Figure 59.

A chain of terms connected by the same relation can often be diagramed by one or more shuttles with small circles at required spots along each shuttle to mark the truth-value lines that are involved. For example, $A \bullet \sim B \bullet D$ can be graphed in the manner of Figure 60.

If the chain stands alone as a complete premise, we can of course

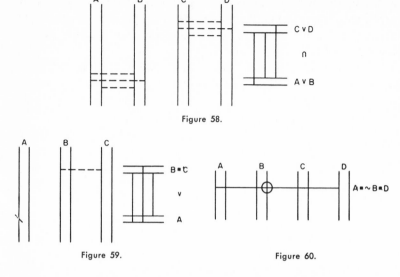

Figure 58.

Figure 59.   Figure 60.

place X's on each truth-value line involved in the chain. If part of a compound statement, however, the shuttle must be dotted and the X's cannot be added until we discover that the entire chain is a valid relation. The intersection point surrounded by the small circle is treated exactly as if it were the terminal point of a shuttle. The absence of a circle on either of C's truth-value lines indicates that C is not involved in the chain.

A chain of equivalent relations, such as $A \equiv B \equiv C$, can be diagramed as in Figure 61, with two shuttles, using small circles on B's truth-value lines.

Similar procedures can be worked out for statements that tell us only one term in a series is true, or that all the terms cannot be false, or that any combination of truth values is permitted except all true and all false, and so on. In such cases, of course, we are merely showing the valid lines of a truth table for the entire chain of terms. In the above three-term example, we make use of two valid lines of an eight-line table. Consequently, if we found it necessary to negate the chain we would have to replace the two shuttles by the six missing ones.

When there are more than three terms in a chain, the number of shuttles involved may become too troublesome to handle and we may find it simpler to break the chain into parenthetical phrases and diagram them by extending the graph to the right as previously explained. For example, if we interpret the chain $A \lor B \lor C \lor D$ to mean that all the terms cannot be false, we can diagram this as $(A \lor B) \lor (C \lor D)$.

Conversely, we may sometimes find it convenient to take a compound expression such as $A \supset (B \bullet C)$, and instead of diagraming it by extending the graph, we can work out an eight-line truth table for the entire expression and picture it as shown in Figure 62.

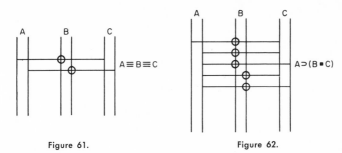

Figure 61.   Figure 62.

This is a diagrammatic way of expanding the original statement to what logicians call its "normal disjunctive" form. Each shuttle in the above diagram represents a valid line of the eight-line truth table. The entire pattern corresponds to the expression $(A \bullet B \bullet C) \lor (\sim A \bullet B \bullet C) \lor (\sim A \bullet B \bullet \sim C) \lor (\sim A \bullet \sim B \bullet C) \lor (\sim A \bullet \sim B \bullet \sim C)$.

When the same terms appear more than once in a statement it often is possible to reduce the statement to a simpler form before diagraming it. For example, the statement $(A \bullet \sim B) \lor (\sim A \bullet \sim B)$ can be diagramed as parenthetical statements connected by the inclusive "or" relation. But since we are dealing with only two terms, and since shuttles belonging to the same binary relation represent disjunctive possibilities, it is much simpler to diagram the statement as in Figure 63.

This is still not the simplest diagram, for we see at once that, regardless of the truth or falsity of A, B must be false, whereas knowing B to be false tells us nothing about A. Consequently, we can picture the original assertion simply by making a cross on B's F line (Figure 64).

In other words, the formula $(A \bullet \sim B) \lor (\sim A \bullet \sim B) \equiv \sim B$ is a tautology. Thus we see how the network graph can be used as a visual aid in the task of reducing a statement to its most economical or "logically powerful" form. There are a number of rules that can be followed for the elimination of unnecessary shuttles and other steps involved in the "minimizing" of a statement, but the subject is too complicated to go into here.

For long statements containing parentheses within parentheses, the graph may be extended as far as we please by adding additional truth-value lines, alternating horizontal with vertical graphs in the stair-step fashion shown in Figure 65.

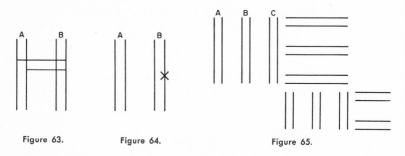

Figure 63.　　　　　Figure 64.　　　　　　Figure 65.

This stair-step procedure will obviously take care of as many parenthetical levels as desired. All patterns must of course be shown as tentative (half crosses and dotted shuttles) except for the final relation shown in the lower right corner. This relation alone is not tentative and therefore is expressed by solid shuttles.

We cannot go into all the details involved in solving problems expressed by compound statements, but the reader who is sufficiently interested will not find it difficult to work out his own rules. The following important rules should make clear the general nature of the procedure.

1. If the truth values of all individual terms within a parenthetical statement are known, and they conform to one of the dotted shuttles for that statement, then the entire statement is known to be true.

In some cases, knowing the truth value of one term only is sufficient to establish the truth value of the entire function. In the relation of implication, for example, the falsity of A is all the information we need to know that $A \supset B$ is a true function because there are two shuttles leading from A's F line. In other words, there is a shuttle for FT and another for FF; so regardless of whether B is true or false, there will be a shuttle to represent the combination. In similar fashion the truth of B is sufficient to tell us that $A \supset B$ must be true. We encounter similar situations with $A \mid B$ and $A \lor B$. We can phrase the procedure as follows. When we know the truth value of one term only, and there are two shuttles leading from this truth-value line, we can then affirm the truth of the entire binary function. If there is only one shuttle, we lack sufficient information to do this.

2. If the terms are known to have a combination of truth values *not* indicated by a shuttle, the entire relation is known to be false.

3. Whenever a parenthetical statement is known to be true, either because of knowledge of its terms or because it is found to be true in the process of exploring the entire structure, its shuttles are changed to solid lines or its half crosses to crosses. The truth of the entire statement is then indicated by a cross mark on the T line in the pair of truth-value lines (to the right or below) that correspond to the statement.

4. Whenever a parenthetical statement is known to be false, in either of the two ways mentioned above, we add the missing shuttle or shuttles in solid lines. The falsity of the entire relation is then indicated by a cross mark on the F line in the pair of truth-value lines that correspond to the statement.

Let us illustrate the entire procedure with an elementary problem of a type not hitherto considered. Suppose we wish to know whether the statement $(A \supset B) \supset (B \supset A)$ is a valid theorem. If it is, then it must hold for all possible value combinations of A and B. To determine this we first diagram the statement as in Figure 66.

We must now test this structure for the four possible combinations of values for A and B—a diagrammatic procedure corresponding to the matrix method of testing a theorem. If none of these combinations produces a contradiction, we know the structure represents a valid logical law. Our testing procedure will show that the combinations TT, TF, and FF are all consistent, but when we test for FT we encounter a contradiction. Let us see how this occurs.

The first step in testing for FT is to make a cross on A's F line and a cross on B's T line as shown in the illustration below. Since this combination is represented by a shuttle in the pattern for the lower statement, we know that the lower statement is true. Consequently, we change its dotted shuttles to solid ones and indicate the truth of the relation by a cross on the corresponding T line on the right. Since there is but one shuttle attached to this line, we must follow the shuttle to the T line of the upper pair of horizontal truth-value lines. This tells us that the upper statement, $B \supset A$, is also true. We indicate this by putting a cross on its T line and changing its shuttles to solid lines. The graph should now look like Figure 67.

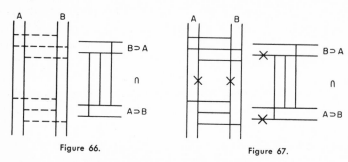

Figure 66.   Figure 67.

We are obviously involved in a contradiction. For if we explore A's F line, affirmed with a cross mark, we encounter a single shuttle that carries us to B's F line. But this contradicts our assumption that B is true. Similarly, the single shuttle attached to B's T line will carry us to A's T line, contradicting our assumption that A is false.

Examination of the structure could have proceeded in other ways, but the results would have been the same. For example, we might have begun by finding the upper relation false, in which case the vertical shuttles on the right would have forced us to conclude that the lower relation was also false. Knowing it to be false, we supply in a solid line the missing shuttle. This in turn tells us that A is true and B false, thus contradicting our original assumptions about A and B. Of course it does not matter in the least how we go about exploring the structure. As soon as we encounter a contradiction, we know that the statement we are testing is not a law. If we do not come upon a contradiction, as, for example, in testing $(A \supset B) \vee (B \supset A)$, then we know it is a valid theorem.

Syllogisms can be tested in this way to determine if they are laws, but the process is awkward, especially if particular statements are involved. To give one example, suppose we wished to test the validity of the syllogism:

> All A is B
> No B is C
> Therefore, no A is C

This can be stated in the propositional calculus as the following theorem: $[(A \supset B) \bullet B \mid C] \supset A \mid C$. When we test it for the eight possible combinations of values for the three terms, it proves to be valid in all cases. A particular statement, such as "Some A is B," must be handled as a disjunction—in this case, $(A \bullet B \bullet C) \vee (A \bullet B \bullet \sim C)$.

It should be unnecessary to point out that all the rules given in this chapter for the manipulation of network diagrams apply only to a material interpretation of implication. They do not apply to a system of "strict implication" such as proposed by Clarence I. Lewis, in which the consequent of an implication must be formally deducible from the antecedent. In strict implication, knowing the truth values of individual terms in a conditional relation is not sufficient to tell you the truth value of the entire statement except when the antecedent is known to be true and the consequent false (in which case the implication is known to be false). I suspect that the network method can, with the adoption of suitable conventions, be adapted to strict implication logics, but this is a use for the method that is beyond my capacities to explore.

It is also possible, I think, to combine this system with the Venn circles so that problems involving a mixture of class-inclusion statements and truth-value statements can be handled together. Still another interesting possibility is that of extending the network method to take care of multivalued logics that are based on truth-table matrices.[2] For example, a three-value logic could be diagramed by increasing the number of truth-value lines under each term from two to three. Since shuttles in such a logic represent two types of relations, true and "indeterminate" (or whatever one wishes to call the third value), it will be necessary to distinguish two types of shuttle lines. This could be done by making "true" shuttles solid and using a saw-toothed line for the new value.

Exactly what pattern of shuttles to use for a given function will depend on the type of three-value logic we are considering. Here we enter the realm of Lewis Carroll's Humpty Dumpty, for whom words meant just what he wanted them to mean. In multivalued logics, connectives such as "and" and "implies" cease to have intuitive meanings and are used merely to express a specific matrix pattern of values. To make this a bit clearer, let us reflect a moment on the meaning of "and" in two-value logic. The assertion "A and B are true" can be diagramed with two cross marks or a single shuttle as shown in Figure 68.

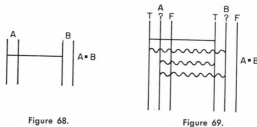

Figure 68.   Figure 69.

This shuttle tells us that the other three possible shuttles represent nonpermissible or "false" combinations of values for A and B; hence they are eliminated from the diagram. In three-value logic the situation is not so simple. In the first place we have nine possible shuttles for every pair of terms. We know that the statement "A and B" requires a solid shuttle from A's T line to B's T line, but how are we to interpret the other eight combinations of values? The answer is that we can interpret them any way we choose, basing our decision on such factors as an analogy with two-value logic, a pleasing symmetry or richness in the pattern, some intended meaning for the third value, and so on. Each interpretation of "and" will involve us in a different brand of three-value logic. Jan Lukasiewicz, Emil Post, and Barkley Rosser have a preference for an "and" that can be represented by the shuttle pattern of Figure 69.

On the other hand, the Russian logician D. A. Bochvar based an interesting three-valued logic on the pattern of Figure 70.

Like the paradoxes of material implication, a great many mysteries of three-value logics are cleared up when we realize that words like "and," "not," and "implies" have only the most tenuous analogy, if any at all, with their meanings in everyday speech. A three-value logic function means nothing more than the particular matrix pattern (in our case, the shuttle pattern) that is permitted by that relation. If instead of saying "*A* implies *B*" in a three-value system we said "*A* galumphs *B*," considerable clarity might result.

Figure 71 shows how the shuttles for "*A* implies *B*" appear when we diagram the relation in the three-value system proposed by Lukasiewicz and Alfred Tarski.

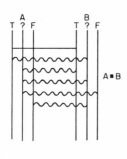

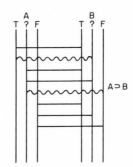

Figure 70.   Figure 71.

There is as little to be gained in trying to understand the "meaning" of this relation as in trying to visualize a four-dimensional cube. The pattern itself is all the meaning the relation need have. It is interesting to note that if we remove all the shuttles that have terminal points on a ? line we are left with the familiar shuttle pattern of two-value implication. There is a sense, therefore, in which the two-value structure is a subsystem of this larger matrix.

Many-valued logics of more than three values, such as Hans Reichenbach's probability logic, would require additional truth-value lines, one for each value in the system. The different types of shuttles could be distinguished by using different colored pencils (corresponding colors could also be used for the value lines). I do not think the difficulties here are insuperable, but perhaps the complexity of rules that would be necessary for manipulating such graphs would make them too unwieldy to be useful.

Even in the humdrum world of two-value logic it is sometimes expedient to graph a problem with value lines that stand for something other than true and false. Suppose we are told that Smith, Jones, and Robinson are professors of physics, mathematics, and philosophy, though not necessarily respectively. A group of premises tells us that, if Jones teaches physics, Robinson teaches mathematics, and so on. One approach to this familiar type of brain teaser would be to make a graph for nine propositions (Smith is a philosophy professor, Smith is a physics professor, etc.), each capable of being true or false. However, since the three faculty posts are taken as mutually exclusive, a simpler approach is to use only three terms (standing for the three men), each with three value lines to represent the three subjects which they teach. In a way, this is solving the problem by a kind of three-value logic, though not a true multivalue system since the relations still must be either true or false.

Lewis Carroll's plan of placing counters on a graph can also be

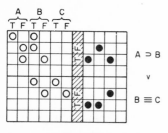

Figure 72.

adapted to the network system. Instead of truth-value lines we have truth-value columns in which counters may be placed to indicate permissible true and false combinations. A sheet of graph paper can be used as the "board," and buttons or beans can serve as counters. The statement $(A \supset B) \lor (B \equiv C)$ would appear on the board as shown in Figure 72.

To indicate the tentative nature of the relations inside parentheses we use counters of a different color from those used for the nontentative relation on the right of the graph. Counters that are one color on one side, another color on the other, would be convenient because then, if we wished to change a relation from tentative to true, we would only have to turn over its counters. Obviously, all rules that apply to the network method can be adapted to the counter method. Although this procedure is in some ways less iconic with propositional logic than the other, in other ways it more closely resembles the matrix method of truth tables. It has the advantage of making it easy to alter the structure in any desired way without the annoyance of having to erase. If one wishes to simplify a structure by eliminating unnecessary shuttles, then it has a decided advantage. Actually, this counter method is really a primitive abacus for performing logic operations; it is as much a "logic machine" as a "diagram."

As we shall see in the chapters to follow, most of the logic machines that have so far been constructed, from Lord Stanhope's syllogism device to modern electrical machines for the propositional calculus, operate by principles that are intimately related to the diagrammatic procedures sketched in this and the preceding chapter.

References

1. All binary functions involving three shuttles can be reduced to two "one-way" shuttles by using arrows to indicate that travel is in one direction only. Thus $A \supset B$ could be shown as:

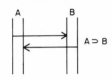 In some cases, this is an efficient type of diagram to use, but it was not introduced in the chapter because it unduly complicates the system and also because it reduces the system's iconicity. In the construction of electrical machines, however, these "one-way" shuttles (circuits made one-way by relays or electronic devices) play an important role.

2. Concerning multivalued logics, the only intelligible popular account known to me is by J. Barkley Rosser, "On the Many-valued Logics," *American Journal of Physics*, Vol. 9, August, 1941, p. 207. For more advanced discussions see Emil Post's classic paper, "Introduction to a General Theory of Elementary Propositions," *American Journal of Mathematics*, Vol. 43, 1921, p. 163; *Symbolic Logic*, by C. I. Lewis and C. H. Langford, 1932; and *Many-valued Logics*, by Rosser and A. R. Turquette, 1952. The latter work contains an excellent selected bibliography.

4: The Stanhope
Demonstrator

Although Ramon Lull made use of rotating disks to facilitate the working of his eccentric system of reasoning, his devices are not "logic machines" in the sense that they can be used for solving problems in formal logic. The inventor of the world's first logic machine, in this stricter sense of the term, was a colorful eighteenth century British statesman and scientist, Charles Stanhope, third Earl Stanhope (1753–1816). His curious device, which he called a "demonstrator," is interesting in more ways than one. Not only could it be used for solving traditional syllogisms by a method closely linked to the Venn circles; it also took care of numerical syllogisms (anticipating De Morgan's analysis of such forms) as well as elementary problems of probability. In addition, it was based on a system of logical notation which clearly foreshadowed Hamilton's technique of reducing syllogisms to statements of identity by making use of negative terms and quantified predicates.

Stanhope's speculations on logic covered a period of some thirty years, but he published nothing about his logical views beyond printing on his own hand press several early chapters of an unfinished work titled *The Science of Reasoning Clearly Explained upon New Principles*. These chapters were circulated only among a few acquaintances. In a letter written shortly before his death he advises a friend not to discuss his logical methods with others lest "some bastard imitation" of his views appear before the publication of his projected work. It was not until sixty years later that one of the earl's contrivances, together with relevant letters and notes, came into the hands of Rev. Robert Harley, who then published an account of the demonstrator and the logic on which it was based. It is from Harley's article, "The Stanhope Demonstrator," *Mind,* Vol. 4, April, 1879, that most of the following account of Lord Stanhope and his unusual device is drawn.

In his day, Stanhope was better known throughout England for his fiery political opinions and confused domestic affairs than for his many scientific inventions. His first wife was the sister of England's young and controversial prime minister, William Pitt.[1] For a time the earl was a supporter of Pitt, but he later broke with the ministry to become a vigorous opponent of most of its measures. As a member of the Revolution Society, formed to honor the Revolution of 1688, his political views were strongly liberal and democratic. His impetuous proposals in the House of Lords were so often and so soundly defeated that he was widely known as the "minority of one," and his thin figure was prominent in the political cartoons of the period. He was an ardent supporter of the French republicans in the early days of the French Revolution. It is said that he even went so far as to discard all the external trappings of his peerage.

At the early age of nineteen he was elected a fellow of the Royal Society and for the rest of his life he devoted a large segment of his time and income to scientific pursuits. His best known inventions were the Stanhope microscopic lens, the Stanhope hand printing press, a monochord for tuning musical instruments, a system for fireproofing buildings, certain improvements in canal locks, a method of stereotyping, and a primitive steamboat. In a book titled *Principles of Electricity,* 1779, he outlines a novel electrical theory of his own. In addition to his logic machine, he also devised an arithmetical calculating machine employing geared wheels.[2]

Before explaining Stanhope's logic demonstrator, it will be necessary first to glance briefly at his logic. It rests on the assumption, later emphasized by George Bentham, William Hamilton, and others, that any proposition in class logic can be interpreted as a statement of identity.[3] Thus if we say "All men are mortal," we can take this to mean that the class of all men is identical to a portion of the class of all mortal things. If we say "Socrates is mortal," we mean that this one man, Socrates, is identical to one of the members of the class of all mortal things. Negative propositions are reduced to identities by changing them to affirmative statements and employing negative terms. For example, "No swans are green" tells us that the class of all swans is identical with a portion of the class of all not-green things.

The following table shows how the four traditional propositions, A,E,I,O, can be rephrased as statements of identity:

A.	All *A* is *B*	All *A* = Some *B*
E.	No *A* is *B*	All *A* = Some not-*B*
I.	Some *A* is *B*	Some *A* = Some *B*
O.	Some *A* is not *B*	Some *A* = Some not-*B*

Stanhope used the term *"holos"* (the Greek word for "whole") to stand for the middle term a syllogism, choosing this word to underscore the fact that the middle term must be universally distributed in at least one premise before it can successfully mediate an inference concerning the other two terms. The other terms are called *"ho"* and *"los"* (*ho* if it is in the first premise, *los* if in the second. The order of premises is immaterial. The first premise is simply the statement first considered).

"The reader will observe," Stanhope writes, "that *ho* as well as *los* may be identic with *holos,* but that neither *ho* nor *los* can ever exceed *holos*."

In Stanhope's terminology, the demonstrator is simply a device for determining what relation of *ho* to *los* can be deduced by relating each term to the *holos*. The contrivance consists of a block of mahogany 4 inches wide, 4½ inches tall, and ¾ inch thick, with a brass plate mounted on the face (Figure 73). In the center

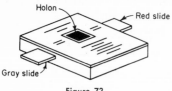

Figure 73.

of the plate is a square window or depression about an inch wide and a half-inch deep. Stanhope calls this window the "holon." It represents "all" of the *holos*, or middle term of whatever syllogism is being examined.

A panel of gray wood stands for the *ho*—the term in the first premise that is not the middle term. It can be pushed into the demonstrator through a slot on the left until it covers part or all of the holon. The *los* (the term in the second premise that is not the middle term) is represented by a panel of transparent red glass that is pushed into the machine through a slot on the right, sliding on top of the gray in case the two slides overlap. Unlike the gray panel, however, it cannot be withdrawn completely from the instrument. As we shall see later, the gray panel can be removed from its slot and inserted through another slot above the holon for working problems in what Stanhope calls the "logic of probability."

A scale from 0 to 10 appears on the brass frame above and to the left of the holon. The same scale also is found on the lower edge of the red slide. Figure 74 shows the face of the demonstrator

Figure 74. Reproduction of the face of Lord Stanhope's demonstrator. (From *Mind*, April, 1879.)

as it appears when both slides are pushed in as far as they will go, the red above the gray and both covering the entire holon.

The working of the device is quite simple. Suppose, for example, we have the following premises:

> No *M* is *A*
> All *B* is *M*

The first step is to convert these premises into affirmative statements of identity, all the terms properly quantified:

> All *M* is some not-*A*
> All *B* is some *M*

We insert the gray panel (which stands for "some not-*A*") into the demonstrator, pushing it to the right until it covers "all" of the holon (which represents *M*). In other words, "some not-*A*" is made identical with all of *M*.

The next step is to push the red slide (all *B*) until it only partially covers the holon, since all of *B* is identical with only part of *M*. Whenever the two slides are forced to overlap, as in this example, the gray panel is visible through the red and we can conclude that an identity has been established between the *ho* and the *los*. In this case we conclude that "all *B*" is identical with "some not-*A*." This is the same as saying "No *B* is *A*" (or "No *A* is *B*"), the traditional valid conclusion of the syllogism. The device, it should be noted, does not show the "weak" conclusions—"Some *B* is not *A*" and "Some *A* is not *B*." These have to be obtained by immediate inference from "No *B* is *A*."

The rules for operating the demonstrator can be summarized as follows:

1. When a premise relates a term to "all" of the middle term, we push the panel for that term over the entire holon.

2. When a premise relates a term to "some" of the middle term, we push the panel for that term over part of the holon.

3. When a premise relates a term to "none" of the middle term (e.g., "No *A* is *M*," or in affirmative form, "All *A* is not-*M*"), we withdraw the panel for that term so that no part of the holon is covered by it.

4. After the two slides are properly adjusted to represent the two premises, we inspect the holon to see if the slides must of necessity overlap. If so, we may then conclude an identity has been

established between the terms represented by the slides. If the slides are not forced to overlap, no identity is established and therefore no conclusion can be drawn.

A few more examples will make the process clearer.

>No *M* is *A*
>No *M* is *B*

In affirmative form this is:

>All *M* is some not-*A*
>All *M* is some not-*B*

The two slides, standing for "some not-*A*" and "some not-*B*" are each pushed over the entire holon. They must overlap; so we conclude that "Some not-*A* is some not-*B*." This is not, of course, a traditional conclusion, for we have committed the fallacy of beginning with two negative premises and so cannot draw a conclusion about the relation of *A* to *B*. Nevertheless, it is a valid conclusion (assuming that the middle term has members), as can be seen easily by making a Venn diagram of the syllogism. We may even go a step further, Stanhope points out, and conclude that as many not-*A*'s are not-*B*'s as there are *M*'s.

In one case only, that of the traditionally troublesome syllogism *Baroco*, the holon must be regarded as "not-*M*" instead of *M*. The two premises of *Baroco:*

>All *A* is *M*
>Some *B* is not *M*

must be converted to:

>All not-*M* is some not-*A*
>Some *B* is some not-*M*

The gray slide (some not-*A*) is pushed over the entire holon, which in this case represents "not-*M*." The red slide (some *B*) is pushed over part of the holon. The two must overlap, indicating the traditional conclusion of *Baroco*, "Some *B* is some not-*A*," or as commonly expressed, "Some *B* is not *A*."

In such fashion the device can be used to demonstrate valid conclusions from two premises or to show that no valid conclusion can be drawn. The task, however, of translating the premises into proper form is so tedious that the device possesses little value either as an efficient means of handling syllogisms or in giving the mind a clear visual understanding of what is happening in syllogistic inference. In such respects it is markedly inferior to the Venn circles, which in some ways it anticipates. On the other hand, owing to its rectangular form, it is more efficient than the Venn circles when used for syllogisms with terms that have numerically definite quantifiers or indefinite quantifiers such as "more than half" or "less than half."

Consider, for example, these premises:

Some *M* is some *A*
Some *M* is some *B*

The gray panel is "some *A*"; the red is "some *B*." Each is pushed only part way over the holon (some *M*). The two slides are not forced to overlap; hence no conclusion can be drawn. Suppose, however, that for "some *M*" in each premise we substitute "most of *M*." In this case, each slide is made to cover "most," or more than half of the holon, and it is apparent that they must overlap to some extent. We therefore can conclude validly that "Some *A* is *B*." This is, of course, an example of one of De Morgan's syllogisms discussed in the second chapter.

To illustrate how the demonstrator may be used for De Morgan's syllogism with numerical quantifiers, let us consider what can be deduced from the following two premises:

8 of 10 pictures are abstractions.
4 of the same 10 pictures are by Picasso.

We let the holon stand for the middle term of "10 pictures." The gray slide (8 abstractions) is pushed in from the left until its right edge reaches 8 on the top scale. In other words, until it covers $\frac{8}{10}$ of the area of the holon. The red slide (4 pictures by Picasso) is pushed in from the right until the number 4 on its lower scale coincides with the right edge of the holon; in other words, until it covers $\frac{4}{10}$ of the holon. Through the red glass we see immediately that the edge of the gray slide is touching the 2 on the red slide's scale, indicating that the overlapping area is $\frac{2}{10}$ of the holon. This is what Stanhope calls, on the face of his device, the "extent of the consequence," namely, the minimum number of objects that belong to both the *ho* and the *los*. Our conclusion, then, is that *at least* two of the abstractions must be by Picasso. Of course there may be more (four is the upper limit because there are only four Picasso pictures), but the demonstrator neatly provides us with a visual demonstration of why two is the lower limit.

If the middle term is less than ten units—say, six units—then we simply regard as our holon only that portion of the aperture which extends from the left side to 6 on the upper scale. The gray slide is unaffected by this, but when we use the red slide we must remember to bring the desired number on its lower edge to the point indicated by 6 on the upper scale rather than to the right edge of the holon. It is clear that numerical syllogisms with terms quantified by numbers higher than ten could be handled in exactly the same manner on demonstrators with scales divided into a larger number of units.

In Stanhope's terminology, the demonstrator operates mechanically on all types of syllogisms according to the following simple rule: "Add *ho* to *los* and subtract *holos*." The machine shows clearly how the rule applies, regardless of whether the terms of the syllogism are quantified by numbers, more or less than half, or "all" and "some."

"Behold, then," the Earl writes in one of his notes, "the luminous perspicuity and most beautiful simplicity of this new system of logic!"

Stanhope's letters and unpublished papers do not give examples of how he used his device for his "logic of probability," but from the rule given at the bottom of the brass face (see Figure 74), it is easy to understand how the instrument must have been employed on such problems. This rule states, "The proportion between the area of the dark red [that is, the overlapping area of the two slides] and the area of the holon, is the probability which results from the gray and red."

Rev. Harley illustrates this in his article with the following elementary problem. We wish to determine the probability that a penny will fall heads both times if we toss it twice.

The holon represents 1 or "certainty." The probability of a head in a single throw is one-half. To show this, the gray slide is removed from the slot on the left, inserted through the slot at the top, then pushed down until its edge reaches 5 on the left-hand scale; that is, until it covers one-half the area of the holon. To represent the chance of a head on the second toss, the red slide is pushed to the left until it also covers one-half the area of the holon. The dark red, or overlapping area of the two slides, is obviously one-fourth of the holon. The chance that the penny will fall heads on both tosses is therefore one-fourth. The same procedure would be used, Harley points out, to give exactly the same answer, if we wanted to know the probability that the coin would fall tails twice, or heads and then tails, or tails and then heads.

As in dealing with numerical syllogisms, probability problems involving fractions that cannot be expressed in tenths could be suitably handled by giving the device whatever type of scale it required. As we shall see in Chapter 9, Stanhope's demonstrator, used in the manner just explained, actually is a crude first attempt at a kind of inductive logic machine.

If for your own amusement you wish to make a demonstrator, Rev. Harley suggests a simple way to go about it. Draw on a sheet of graph paper a square consisting of 100 smaller squares and

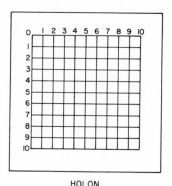

HOLON

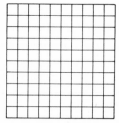

GRAY SLIDE   RED SLIDE

Figures 75 (top), 76, and 77.

label the lattice lines above and on the left as shown in Figure 75. For the gray slide, use a similar square (Figure 76), and for the red slide, a square with a scale indicated on the bottom edge as shown in Figure 77. Harley suggests trimming the lower edge of this square as pictured, so that, when it overlaps the other square, the extent of overlapping can be clearly seen. If you wish, you can color this slide red, and of course all three squares may be mounted on cardboard to make them more durable. They obviously are capable of performing any operation that can be performed on the Stanhope device.

References

1. Stanhope had three daughters by his first wife. The youngest created a scandal by eloping with the family druggist. The Earl was never reconciled to the pair, but Prime Minister Pitt made the druggist controller-general of the customs. The eldest daughter, Lady Hester Lucy Stanhope (1776–1839), kept house for Pitt until his death in 1806. In 1814, with a generous pension from the government, she settled in an abandoned convent in Lebanon where until her death she ruled over her retinue of some thirty servants like an Oriental potentate. For a time she was a political power in the Syrian area. In later years, her interest in the occult intensified, and she claimed to be an inspired prophetess. For fascinating accounts of her beauty, sarcastic wit, arrogance, and legendary exploits, see Alphonse de Lamartine's *Voyages en Orient,* Alexander Kinglake's *Eothen,* and the six volumes of Lady Hester's memoirs prepared after her death by her physician, Dr. Charles Lewis Meryon.

   The fourth Earl Stanhope, Philip Henry (one of Charles's three sons by his second wife), is best known for his espousal of the famous German imposter, Kaspar Hauser. Philip paid for Hauser's education and even wrote a book in German about him.

2. Lord Stanhope either made or had made for him several models of both his logic and arithmetical machines. Photographs of one model of each machine are reproduced opposite page 127 of *Early Science in Oxford,* by Robert W. T. Gunther, Vol. 1, Part 1, 1922. These two models are owned by the Oxford Museum of the History of Science, Old Ashmolean Building, Oxford. A second model of the logic machine is owned by the present Earl Stanhope.

3. A quotation from one of Stanhope's letters gives an amusing insight into the value he placed on recognizing that class propositions could be expressed as identities:

   "When I talk of identity, I do *not* say, as you make me say, *que 'L'âme est l'âme,' car cela ne dit rien,* but I say thus: Example. Suppose I had heard that there was such a thing as a *comet.* I now perceive in the heavens at night *a star with a luminous tail;* that is all I know, and it is by means of that mental description that I distinguish that star from all other stars. I afterwards find my star, so distinguished, described and defined, amongst the stars of some new constellation, and I predicate that that star *has moved fast,* which is a quality of my comet, but which quality of my comet was before to me unknown; that is to say, I aver that 'the star with a luminous tail' and a star which 'moves fast,' that is, which belongs to the *class of stars that move fast,* are IDENTIC. Have I not made an advance in knowledge by my having so perceived, though in point of fact, it is the *same* comet, the *identical* comet, originally described by me incompletely, before I perceived, or could predicate, such identity? *Voilà tout.* Would it not sound to your ears very droll if a person were to say that *that star moving fast* means that it is identic with some star which does *not move fast?* Now if that would be evidently wrong, and if I have by my method *only two opposite classes, viz.,* stars *moving fast* and stars *not moving fast,* if the proposition in question does not mean that the given star is *identic* with a star in the second class, it must mean that it is identic with a star in the first class; for there are *two* classes only. This is my induction in other words."

5:   Jevons's Logic Machine

Ramon Lull was the first to use a mechanical device as an aid to reasoning. Lord Stanhope was the first to use a mechanical device for the solution of problems in formal logic. The next great step in the history of logic machines took place in 1869 when William Stanley Jevons, British economist and logician, produced the first working model of his famous logic machine. It was the first such machine with sufficient power to solve a complicated problem faster than the problem could be solved without the machine's aid.

Jevons was born in Liverpool in 1835, the son of an iron merchant. He interrupted his education at University College, London, to spend five years working for the British mint in Sidney, Australia. In 1859 he returned to University College and, after obtaining a master of arts degree, accepted the post of tutor at Owens College, now the University of Manchester. He soon found himself carrying the double title of "professor of logic and mental and moral philosophy" and "professor of political economy." In 1876 he became professor of political economy at his alma mater, the University College, London, where he remained until he resigned the chair in 1880 because of failing health. Two years later, at the age of only forty-seven, he was drowned while swimming alone off the beach at Bulverhythe, near Hastings.

As an economist, Jevons is regarded as one of the pioneers in the rigorous application of statistical techniques to the study of economic issues. His *Theory of Political Economy,* 1871, is the most important of his many books and papers on economic and political topics. Unfortunately, his valuable contributions to economic theory (especially his trenchant analysis of marginal utility) are less well remembered today than his speculations on the relation of sunspots to business cycles. In the light of present-day knowledge and statistical sophistication, such a theory can only be regarded as eccentric, but we must remember that in Jevons's time it was far from a crank notion. The view that sunspots might influence weather and crops, which in turn would affect the business cycle, then had a plausibility that deserved careful exploration.[1]

In somewhat similar fashion, Jevons's fame as the inventor of a logic machine has tended to obscure the important role he played in the history of both deductive and inductive logic. He was one of the pioneers of modern symbolic logic, and his *Principles of Science,* first issued in 1874, deserves far more recognition than it has today as an important treatise on the philosophy and methods of science. At a time when most British logicians ignored or damned with faint praise the remarkable achievements of George Boole, Jevons was quick to see the importance of Boole's work as well as many of its defects. He regarded Boole's algebraic logic as the greatest advance in the history of the subject since Aristotle. He deplored the fact that Boole's two revolutionary books, published as early as 1847 and 1854, had virtually no effect on the speculations of leading logicians of the time.

On the other hand, Jevons believed (and modern logicians agree with him) that Boole had been led astray by efforts to make his logical notation resemble algebraic notation. "I am quite convinced," Jevons stated in a letter, "that Boole's forms . . . have no real analogy to the similar mathematical expressions." [2] He also saw clearly the weakness in Boole's preference for the exclusive rather than the inclusive interpretation of "or."

It was to overcome what he regarded as unnecessary obscurity and awkwardness in Boole's notation that Jevons devised a method of his own that he called the "method of indirect inference." "I have been able to arrive at exactly the same results as Dr. Boole," he wrote, "without the use of any mathematics; and though the very simple process which I am about to describe can hardly be said to be strictly Dr. Boole's logic, it is yet very similar to it and can prove everything that Dr. Boole proved." [3] Jevons's system, as we shall see, is also very similar to Venn's diagrammatic method as well as a primitive form of the familiar matrix or truth-table technique. Since it underlies Jevons's logic machine, it will be necessary to review it in some detail.

Putting it jocularly, but with a certain amount of justification, one might say that the method is a linking of Lull's *Ars magna* with one of Sherlock Holmes's favorite canons of deduction; namely, that if you eliminate all possible explanations of a crime but one, that one explanation is certain to be correct. As the technique of *reductio ad absurdum,* this procedure is an ancient one, but the realization that it could be applied to the Boolean logic came to Jevons in an almost Lullian-like illumination. "As I awoke in the morning," he recorded in his journal in 1866, "the sun was shining brightly into my room. There was a consciousness on my mind that I was the discoverer of the true logic of the future. For a few minutes I felt a delight such as one can seldom hope to feel." [4]

The easiest way to explain Jevons's logic is to give a few examples of how it operates. Let us consider first the two syllogistic premises, All *A* is *B,* and No *B* is *C.* Our first step is to make a Lullian table that exhausts all possible combinations of *ABC* and their negations. Since Jevons always symbolized a negation by using a lower-case letter (a convention which he borrowed from De Morgan) we shall adopt this practice here. The table appears as follows:

ABC
ABc
AbC
Abc
aBC
aBc
abC
abc

These eight classes correspond of course to the eight compartments of Venn's three-circle diagram (including the area representing *abc*, which lies outside the circles). Jevons at first called such an exhaustive list an "abecedarium," but students found this difficult to pronounce so he soon discarded it for "logical alphabet." [5] His procedure for analyzing the two premises corresponds precisely with Venn's procedure in shading compartments on the intersecting circles.[6] The first premise, All *A* is *B,* tells us that the classes *Abc* and *AbC* are empty; therefore we draw a line through them. Similarly, the second premise, No *B* is *C,* will eliminate classes *ABC* and *aBC*. The logical alphabet will now look like this:

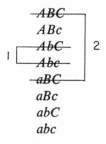

The final step is to inspect the remaining classes, all consistent with the premises, to see what we can determine about the relation of *A* to *C*. We note at once that "No *A* is *C*" (that is, there are no remaining combinations containing both *A* and *C*); hence this is a valid inference from the premises. On the assumption that none of the three classes are empty, we may also conclude that "Some *A* is not *C*," since the only class containing an *A* is one that contains a *c*. This is what classic logic calls a "weak" conclusion because it can be derived by immediate inference from the universal conclusion "No *A* is *C*." We may also draw various other non-traditional inferences such as "Some not-*A* is *C*." Like Venn and Lewis Carroll, Jevons was proud of the fact that his system was not limited to the traditional syllogistic conclusions, providing all possible inferences from the original premises.

In handling particular ("some") statements, the logical alphabet does not operate as smoothly as the Venn circles. The premise "Some *A* is *B*" does not eliminate any classes, but simply states that, of the two combinations *ABc* and *ABC,* at least one and possibly both have members. Perhaps the best procedure is to draw circles around these combinations (corresponding to the placing of *X*'s in the cells of Venn circles), remembering that, when two classes are circled, they cannot both be empty. Jevons suggested some other procedures for handling these troublesome "somes," all rather clumsy and of no special interest.

In working with binary truth-value relations, Jevons's system operates more efficiently than with class logic. In explaining its application to the propositional calculus we shall take the same liberties we took in explaining how the Venn diagrams could be similarly used. Like Venn and most of the other logicians of his time, Jevons confined his attention almost exclusively to class logic. He combined statements of class inclusion (though he preferred, like Stanhope, to think of such statements in terms of identity of part or all of one class with part or all of another) with conjunctive or disjunctive assertions (e.g., All A and B is either C or D) but almost never worked with truth-value relations alone.

The trend toward a truth-value calculus was making a faint beginning in Jevons's time, but unfortunately he failed completely to see its significance.[7] Perhaps, like Boole, he was too intent on keeping his notation in the form of equations. For example, Jevons's expression for the statement "All A is B" is the equation $A = AB$, meaning that all of class A is identical with the class of things that are both A and B. This equational form then permitted him to substitute for any term or statement any other term or statement that was equivalent. Jevons called this "the substitution of similars." (Statements were "similar" for him if they removed the same combinations from his logical alphabet. Modern logicians would call them equivalent or tautological.) The following passage from his *Studies in Deductive Logic,* p. xv, in which he refers to the new calculus of Hugh MacColl,[8] reveals how decisively Jevons turned his back on the trend toward truth-value analysis:

> Mr. MacColl rejects equations in favor of *implications;* thus my $A = AB$ becomes with him $A:B$, or A implies B. Even his letter-terms differ in meaning from mine, since his letters denote propositions, not things. Thus $A:B$ asserts that the statement A implies the statement B, or that whenever A is true, B is also true. It is difficult to believe that there is any advantage in these innovations; certainly, in preferring implications to equations, Mr. MacColl ignores the necessity of the equation for the application of the Principle of Substitution. His proposals seem to me to tend towards throwing Formal Logic back into its ante-Boolian confusion.

Because of his preference for what he called "equational logic," we shall look in vain through Jevons's works for problems of a truth-value nature. Ironically, these are precisely the problems that are the easiest to solve by his method. The following simple examples should make clear how such problems are handled. We are given these premises:

> If and only if *A* is true, then *B* is true.
> Either *B* or *C*, but not both, are true.
> *A* is false.

We wish to know what we may infer about *B* and *C*.

As before, the first step is to write down the logical alphabet for three terms. The first premise tells us that we must eliminate all combinations containing *Ab* and *aB*. The second premise eliminates all combinations containing *BC* and *bc*.[9] The third premise excludes all combinations containing *A*. The alphabet will now look like this:

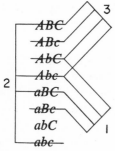

Inspection of the one remaining line of the alphabet shows clearly that *B* must be false and *C* true.

The method is essentially the same as the method described in Chapter 2 by which Venn circles may be used for truth-value logic. Both methods correspond closely to a truth-table analysis. The logical alphabet is simply another way of symbolizing all the possible combinations of truth values. Each premise forces us to eliminate certain lines of this "truth table." What remain are of course the lines that are consistent with the premises. If the premises contain a contradiction, then all the lines will be eliminated just as all the compartments will become shaded if contradictory truth-value premises are diagramed on Venn circles.[10] Jevons likes to call his system a "combinatorial logic," and although he did not apply it to propositional functions, he clearly grasped the principles of matrix analysis that had eluded Boole even though it was implied in his formula for expanding a function. Dr. Wolfe Mays, senior lecturer in philosophy at the University of Manchester (and, as we shall learn later, a coinventor of England's first electric logic machine), is of the opinion that Jevons was the first to make use of matrix analysis.[11]

To increase the efficiency of his combinatorial method, Jevons devised a number of laborsaving devices, culminating in the construction of his logic machine. For example, he suggested having a rubber stamp made of the logical alphabet for three terms, another stamp for four. This eliminates the annoyance of having to jot down all the combinations each time you tackle a new problem. For a problem of five terms, you have only to make two impressions with the *ABCD* stamp, heading one of them *E* and the other *e*. (Venn also suggested having rubber stamps made for his circular figures. See his *Symbolic Logic*, revised 1894 edition, p. 135.)

As early as 1863 Jevons was using a "logical slate." This was a slate on which a logical alphabet was permanently engraved so that problems could be solved by chalking out the inconsistent lines. Still another device, suggested to Jevons by a correspondent, is to pencil the alphabet along the extreme edge of a sheet of paper, then cut the sheet between each pair of adjacent combinations. When a combination is to be eliminated, it is simply folded back out of sight.

Jevons's "logical abacus" (most fully described in his book *The Substitution of Similars*, 1869) was a laborsaving device that required only the addition of keys, levers, and pulleys to become a logic machine. The abacus consisted of small rectangular wooden boards, all the same size, and each bearing a different combination of true and false terms. The boards were lined up on a rack. An arrangement of pegs on the side of each board was such that one could insert a ruler under the pegs and quickly pick out whatever group of boards one wished to remove from the rack. The device was really a primitive form of an IBM punch-card machine, and suggests how easily such a sorting mechanism could be adapted to solving logic problems by the Jevons method.

Jevons's "logical piano," as he sometimes called the machine, was built for him by a "young clockmaker in Salford" in 1869.[12] The following year he demonstrated the machine at a meeting of the Royal Society of London, explaining its construction and working in a paper titled "On the Mechanical Performance of Logical Inference." The paper was printed in full, together with plates show-

.ing details of the machine's construction, in the society's *Philosophical Transactions,* Vol. 160, 1870, p. 497. This paper was later reprinted in Jevons's posthumously published *Pure Logic and Other Minor Works,* 1890. (Summaries of the paper appeared in the society's *Proceedings,* Vol. 18, Jan. 20, 1870, p. 166, and in *Nature,* Vol. 1, Jan. 27, 1870, p. 343.)

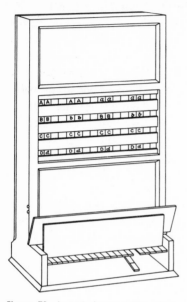

In appearance Jevons's machine resembles a miniature upright piano about 3 feet high (Figure 78). On the face of the piano are openings through which one can see letters representing the 16 possible combinations of four terms and their negatives. (Each combination forms a vertical row of four terms.) The keyboard consists of 21 keys arranged as shown in Figure 79.

The four terms, in positive and negative forms, are represented by eight "letter keys" on the left, and eight letter keys in mirror-image order on the right. The remaining five keys are called "operation keys." The "copula" in the center is pressed to indicate the sign of equality connecting left and right sides of an equation. The "full stop" on the extreme right is pressed after a complete equation has been fed to the machine. When the "finis" key on the ex-

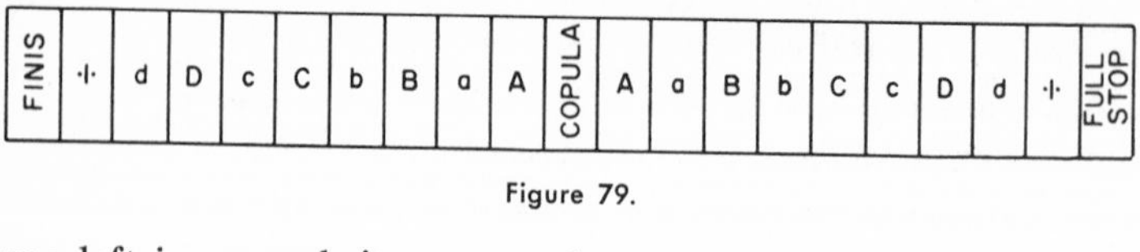

Figure 78. Jevons's logic machine. (From frontispiece of *Principles of Science,* 1874, by William S. Jevons.)

FINIS	·|·	d	D	c	C	b	B	a	A	COPULA	A	a	B	b	C	c	D	d	·|·	FULL STOP

Figure 79.

treme left is pressed, it restores the machine to its original condition. The next-to-end keys on both sides represent the inclusive "or" which Jevons symbolized by ·|·. They are used whenever the "or" relation occurs within either the left or right sides of an equation.

To operate the machine it is only necessary to press the keys in the order indicated by the terms of an equation. For example, let us consider the equation $A = AB$, which as we have seen was Jevons's notation for "All A is B." To feed this to the machine we press the following keys in order: A (on the left), copula, A (on the right), B (on the right), full stop. This action automatically eliminates from the face of the machine all combinations of terms inconsistent with the proposition just fed to the machine. Additional equations are handled in exactly the same manner. After all premises have been fed to the device, its face is then inspected to determine what conclusions can be drawn. This is by no means a complete description of the technique for operating the machine, but it should suffice to indicate in a general way how the machine is handled. The interested reader can learn further details by consulting the references cited above.

Jevons did not think that his machine had any practical use, owing to the fact that complex logical questions seldom arise in everyday life. But he did feel that it was valuable as a classroom device for demonstrating the nature of logical analysis, and also that it furnished a convincing proof of the superiority of Boolean logic over that of Aristotle. The following lengthy quotation (*Principles of Science*, pp. 113 ff.) is striking because it reveals how clearly Jevons grasped the revolutionary character of Boole's work as well as many of its defects:

The time must come when the inevitable results of the admirable investigations of the late Dr. Boole must be recognized at their true value, and the plain and palpable form in which the machine presents those results will, I hope, hasten the time. Undoubtedly Boole's life marks an era in the science of human reason. It may seem strange that it had remained for him first to set forth in its full extent the problem of logic, but I am not aware that anyone before him had treated logic as a symbolic method for evolving from any premises the description of any class whatsoever as defined by those premises. In spite of several serious errors into which he fell, it will probably be allowed that Boole discovered the true and general form of logic, and put the science substantially into the form which it must hold for evermore. He thus effected a reform with which there is hardly anything comparable in the history of logic between his time and the remote age of Aristotle.

Nevertheless, Boole's quasi-mathematical system could hardly be regarded as a final and unexceptionable solution of the problem. Not only did it require the manipulation of mathematical symbols in a very intricate and perplexing manner, but the results when obtained were devoid of demonstrative force, because they turned upon the employment of unintelligible symbols, acquiring meaning only by analogy. I have also pointed out that he imported into his system a condition concerning the exclusive nature of alternatives, which is not necessarily true of logical terms. I shall have to show in the next chapter that logic is really the basis of the whole science of mathematical reasoning, so that Boole inverted the true order of proof when he proposed to infer logical truths by algebraic processes. It is wonderful evidence of his mental power that by methods fundamentally false he should have succeeded in reaching true conclusions and widening the sphere of reason.

The mechanical performance of logical inference affords a demonstration both of the truth of Boole's results and of the mistaken nature of his mode of deducing them. Conclusions which he could obtain only by pages of intricate calculation, are exhibited by the machine after one or two minutes of manipulation. And not only are those conclusions easily reached, but they are demonstratively true, because every step of the process involves nothing more obscure than the three fundamental Laws of Thought.

It is not surprising that Jevons's logic machine, being the first of its kind, would have defects that could be remedied by later machines operating on essentially the same principles. By insisting that statements be fed to the machine in a clumsy equational form, it is made unnecessarily complicated. There is no efficient procedure for feeding "some" propositions to the machine. The mechanism does not permit of easy extension to a larger number of terms. (Jevons once contemplated building a machine for ten terms but abandoned the project when it became clear that the device would occupy the entire wall space of one side of his study.)

A more serious objection to the machine, and one that may not permit of remedy within the framework of Jevons's combinatorial logic, was voiced by the British philosopher Francis H. Bradley in a section on the machine in his *The Principles of Logic*, 1883. As a conclusion, the machine merely exhibits all the consistent lines of the logical alphabet (i.e., all the valid lines of a truth table for the combined premises). It does not perform the additional step of analyzing these lines so that one can see the desired conclusion. The process of analyzing the consistent combinations to determine which terms are true and which are false, or even to find the conclusion of a syllogism, is often as laborious as solving the problem itself. In many cases the valid combinations will not provide true and false values for individual terms but will give a series of consistent combinations that can be condensed into a simpler, more "powerful" logical statement. For example, the machine may reveal the following valid combinations: *AB, Ab, aB*. It does not have the power to reduce this answer to the simpler statement, "Either *A* or *B*, or both, are true" (*A* v *B*). In simple cases such as this, one can easily see the relation that is involved, but in more complicated cases, the task of reducing the answer to compact form is not an easy one. In *Principles of Science* Jevons discusses this task in terms of what he calls the "inverse problem," identifying it (not very successfully) with the process of induction. He does not relate the problem to his machine, though clearly it would be of great value to have a mechanical method of performing these desired reductions.

Jevons himself suggested a crude pencil and paper technique of reducing statements (*Principles of Science*, p. 139) comparing it with the "sieve of Eratosthenes" by which one can search for prime numbers. Later logicians have devised better methods, and although no mechanical device has been built for performing these operations, we shall see in Chapter 8 that electric "minimizing machines" have been constructed.

References

1. In a study of British trade from 1721 to 1878 Jevons found 16 crises in 157 years, giving an average cycle of 10.466 which corresponded closely to estimates in his time of the sunspot cycle. A more complicated version of the theory was set forth by Jevons's son in 1909 to accommodate new data that did not conform to his father's theory. After that, works on the solar causes of boom and bust seem to appear in cycles of 4½ years.

    Owing to vagueness in deciding what constitutes a crisis and exactly when it begins and ends, it is as easy to squeeze economic data into a desired pattern as it is to squeeze historical facts into the construction of the Great Pyramid of Egypt. Henry L. Moore, a Columbia University economist, in a book published in 1923, found an eight-year business cycle which he correlated with the transits of Venus across the sun. Harvard economist Felix I. Shaffner, in the November, 1934, issue of the *Quarterly Journal of Economics,* correlated depressions with sunspots. Two major busts that did not fit his pattern were blamed on volcanic eruptions that screened off solar radiation by filling the atmosphere with dust. Shaffner predicted the next great depression in 1944.

    More recently, *Sunspots in Action,* by Harlan T. Stetson of the Massachusetts Institute of Technology, linked economic depression to mental depression, in turn conditioned by a ten-year sunspot cycle. Stetson warned against the next big crash in 1951.

2. *The Letters and Journal of W. Stanley Jevons,* 1886, p. 350. The book is edited by Jevons's wife who, it is interesting to note, was the daughter of the founder and first owner of the *Manchester Guardian.*

3. *Elementary Lessons in Logic,* 1870, Lesson 23. No English logic text has enjoyed a wider popularity than this. It has had 35 reprintings and is still in print.

4. Quoted by W. Mays and D. P. Henry in their excellent exposition of Jevons's logical views, "Jevons and Logic," *Mind,* Vol. 62, October, 1953, p. 484.

5. Jevons was much intrigued by the formal properties of his logical alphabet. In *Principles of Science* he devotes considerable space to showing its similarities to Pascal's triangle of numbers, and emphasizing that its underlying duality is simply another version of the ancient practice of classifying things by a principle of dichotomy. "Some interest attaches to the history of the Tree of Porphyry and Ramus," he writes, "because it is the prototype of the Logical Alphabet which lies at the basis of logical method" (p. 703).

6. Jevons's method was worked out before Venn's diagrammatic procedure; so there is more justification for regarding the Venn circles as a diagrammatic form of Jevons's alphabet than the alphabet as a notational method of handling Venn's system. Both men, however, looked upon their respective systems as stemming from the work of Boole.

7. This is not meant to imply that the logic of propositions had its origin in this trend. There are hints of such a logic as far back as Aristotle. In the Stoic-Megaric school it reached a high stage of development, including explicit recognition of different kinds of implication, of disjunction in both exclusive and inclusive forms, as well as other truth-value functions and a number of elementary equivalence formulas. The Stoic-Megaric school was as disinterested in Aristotle's class logic as any modern logician. Sextus Empiricus quotes a third century B.C. remark by the head of the Alexandrian Library, that "even the crows on the rooftops are cawing over which conditional is true." See chap. 15 of *Ancient Formal Logic,* by I. M. Bocheński, Amsterdam, 1951.

8. MacColl made many valuable contributions toward an efficient notation for the propositional calculus in articles published only in British newspapers and magazines. Alonzo Church credits him with having developed the first true propositional calculus, and J. Barkley Rosser has recently called attention to MacColl's astonishing analysis, as early as 1896, of a three-value logic using the values "necessary," "impossible," and "possible but not necessary."

9. In one of his letters (*The Letters and Journal of W. Stanley Jevons,* p. 350) Jevons contrasts his notation for the exclusive "or" with Boole's notation to show the greater simplicity of his method over Boole's. Jevons used the symbol $\cdot | \cdot$ for inclusive disjunction. He was therefore able to express any binary relation by the simple expedient of using this symbol to join together the required combinations of true and false terms. Thus his notation for the exclusive "or" was $Ab \cdot | \cdot aB$. Boole's way of symbolizing the same relation was $x(1 - y) + y(1 - x)$. In *Studies in Deductive Logic* Jevons gives a complete matrix analysis of the 256 possible relations involving three terms, expressing each relation both in equational form and in terms of the valid lines of its truth table.

10. This holds only for the propositional calculus. In class logic a contradiction is revealed in two ways: (1) when all the combinations specified by a "some" proposition are eliminated by a universal proposition, and (2) when a class known to have members is declared empty by the elimination of all combinations containing the capital letter for that class.

11. The answer to the question of who was the first to use a matrix method depends of course on how broadly or narrowly the term "matrix method" is defined. As Venn points out (*Symbolic Logic,* revised 1894 edition, p. 415), C. A. Semler, in an 1811 German work, suggested the procedure of listing all possible combinations of terms, then striking out those that are contradicted by the premises, a clear anticipation of Jevons's method. If by "matrix method" we mean nothing more than recognition of the alternate possible combinations of truth values for a given binary function, then this recognition goes all the way back to the ancient Stoic-Megaric school. A truth table for material implication, for example, is given by Sextus Empiricus to define the meaning of a conditional statement as it was understood by Philo of Megara.

    The fact remains, however, that Jevons was probably the first to make extensive use of what is substantially a truth-table method for solving problems, even though its first explicit application to truth-value statements came later. In Jevons's unpublished notes, Dr. W. Mays has pointed out, he even used the now familiar notational device of marking lines of his alphabet with 1 or 0 to indicate their truth or falsity.

12. In 1914 Jevons's original machine was given by his son to the Science Museum, South Kensington, London, but in 1934 it was transferred to the Oxford Museum of the History of Science, Old Ashmolean Building, Oxford, where it is now on display.

6: Marquand's Machine and Others

The Reverend John Venn did not have a high opinion of Jevons as a logician. "Excellent as much of Jevons' work is," Venn wrote (*Symbolic Logic*, revised 1894 edition, p. 165), "—especially as regards the principles of physical and economical science,—I cannot but hold that in the domain of logic his inconsistencies and contradictions are remarkable." There was a strong element of rivalry between the two men; hence it is not surprising to find Venn dismissing Jevons's logic machine as essentially trivial.

I have no high estimate myself [he writes, *op.cit.*, p. 133], of the interest or importance of what are sometimes called logical machines, and this on two grounds. In the first place, it is very seldom that intricate logical calculations are practically forced upon us; it is rather we who look about for complicated examples in order to illustrate our rules and methods. In this respect logical calculations stand in marked contrast with those of mathematics, where economical devices of any kind may subserve a really valuable purpose by enabling us to avoid otherwise inevitable labour. Moreover, in the second place, it does not seem to me that any contrivances at present known or likely to be discovered really deserve the name of logical machines. It is but a very small part of the entire process, which goes to form a piece of reasoning, which they are capable of performing. For, if we begin from the beginning, that process would involve four tolerably distinct steps. There is, first, the statement of our data in accurate logical language. This step deserves to be reckoned, since the variations of popular language are so multitudinous, and the terms often so ambiguous, that the data may need careful consideration before they can be reduced to form. Then, secondly, we have to throw these statements into a form fit for the engine to work with—in this case to reduce each proposition to its elementary denials. It would task the energies of any machine to deal at once with the premises employed even in such simple examples as we have offered, if they were presented to it in their original form. Thirdly, there is the combination or further treatment of our premises after such reduction. Finally, the results have to be interpreted or read off. This last generally gives rise to much opening for skill and sagacity; for . . . in most cases there are many ways of reading off the answer. It then becomes a question of tact and judgment which of these is the simplest and best. . . . I hardly see how any machine can hope to assist us except in the third of these steps; so that it seems very doubtful whether any thing of this sort really deserves the name of a logical engine.

Venn goes on to say that "So little trouble is required to sketch out a fresh diagram for ourselves on each occasion, that it is really not worth while to get a machine to do any part of the work for us. Still as some persons have felt much interest in such attempts, it seemed worth while seeing how the thing could be effected here." He then suggests several mechanical procedures of his own. First, the use of a rubber stamp to form the intersecting circles. Second, draw the desired diagrams on thin board, then cut out the compartments so they fit together like a jigsaw puzzle. Instead of shading compartments, you now can remove the cell in question. Third, he gives a picture (reproduced in Figure 80) of what he calls a "logical-diagram machine."

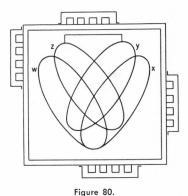

Figure 80.

This machine is merely a three-dimensional form of the jigsaw device. The individual pieces are parts of intersecting elliptical cylinders held in place at the top of a box by sixteen pegs on the sides of the box. To eliminate a cell, you pull out the proper peg, allowing the wooden piece to drop to the bottom of the box. The box is turned upside-down to bring all the blocks back into position for a fresh problem. The picture shows a cross section of the box looking down from above. You will note that the outside compartment is here represented by a closed cell held in place by the top left-hand peg. Venn was of the opinion that this device "would succeed in doing all that can be rationally expected of any logic machine."

As Venn himself recognized, his logic box was simply a mechanical way of handling a Venn diagram. It is surprising that Venn did not think of placing counters on his diagrams, after the manner of Lewis Carroll's method, since this is much simpler than the contrivances he proposed and has the additional advantage that counters of two different colors may be used—one to show that a cell has no members, the other to indicate cells involved in particular ("some") assertions. Although it is true that Venn's devices can perform any of the operations possible on Jevons's logic machine, Venn would not permit himself to appreciate the fact that Jevons's machine was a pioneer effort to work out a mechanical laborsaving method in which desired operations could be effected merely by pressing keys.

The first real advance over Jevons's machine was made by Allan Marquand (1853–1924). The son of Henry G. Marquand, a prominent American philanthropist and art collector, Allan Marquand began his teaching career as a fellow in logic and ethics at Johns Hopkins University. He became a tutor of logic at Princeton University in 1881, but soon abandoned logic to become (in 1883) a professor of art and archeology at Princeton. His books include a *Textbook of the History of Sculpture*, 1896; *Greek Architecture*, 1909; and several books on della Robbia, the famous Florentine sculptor, and his family.

The first logical device built by Marquand is of no special interest. It was merely a more elaborate version of Venn's logical-diagram machine, making use of 256 separate wooden parts to accommodate eight terms. In 1881 he turned his attention toward a machine of the Jevons type, describing the final outcome of his labors in a brief article titled "A New Logical Machine," in the *Proceedings of the American Academy of Arts and Sciences*, Vol. 21, 1885, p. 303. The following account of his machine is taken from this paper.

A crude first model was built by Marquand some time in 1881; then during the winter of 1881–1882 an improved and final model was constructed for Marquand by his friend Prof. Charles G. Rockwood, Jr., of Princeton's department of mathematics. "The machine was made from the wood of a red-cedar post," Marquand tells us, "which once formed part of the enclosure of Princeton's oldest homestead."

Photographs of front and back views of this machine, as it appears today, are reproduced in Figures 81 and 82. In external appearance it resembles a smaller version of Jevons's "logical piano," standing only a trifle more than a foot high, about eight inches wide, and six inches from front to back. The inner mechanism (Figure 82) consists of an ingenious arrangement of rods and

Figure 81. Marquand's logic machine, front view.

Figure 82. Marquand's logic machine, back view, opened to show interior.

levers connected by catgut strings, together with small pins and spiral springs.

Like Jevons's machine it is designed for four terms. The sixteen possible combinations of true and false terms are represented by sixteen rotating pointers on the face of the machine. These pointers are labeled in accordance with Marquand's logic diagram which he had described in a paper published earlier in 1881 (see Figure 33). The method of labeling is easily understood. The pointer in the upper left corner (see Figure 81) stands for *ABCD*. Next to it on the right *AbCD*, then *aBcD*, and so on until *abcd* is reached at the lower right corner. Each pointer can be raised to a horizontal position, pointing leftward, to indicate that the combination is "true" (consistent with the premises), or dropped to a vertical position, pointing downward, to indicate a "false" combination (one excluded by the premises).

The keyboard consists of ten keys only, labeled as shown in Figure 83.

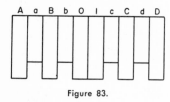

Figure 83.

The four terms (capital letters) and their negatives (lower case letters) are represented by eight keys, the keys for the negatives being shorter than the others. The remaining two keys, marked 1 (the "restoration key") and 0 (the "destruction key"), are called "operation keys." Their use will become clear in a moment.

Before a problem is fed to the machine, all pointers must first be raised to horizontal position. This is done by pressing the two operation keys simultaneously, then releasing first the 1 key, then the 0 key.

Each premise is now fed to the machine in negative form. For example, suppose we wish to impress upon the machine the premise $A \supset B$. This can be restated in negative form by saying that a true A cannot combine with a false B. In other words, all combinations containing Ab must be eliminated from the face of the machine. This is simply done as follows. We press simultaneously the keys for A and b; then while still holding them down with one hand, the other hand presses the 0, or destruction, key. Immediately all pointers representing combinations containing Ab drop to a vertical position. The face of the machine then appears as shown in Figure 84.

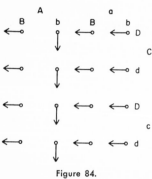

Figure 84.

Each succeeding premise is handled in exactly the same manner. After all premises have been fed to the machine, the pointers indicate what combinations, if any, are consistent with the premises, and desired conclusions can be obtained by inspection of the machine's face. In principle, therefore, the machine operates as does Jevons's device by identifying the valid lines of Jevons's "logical alphabet" or what in modern terms would be called the "true" lines of a truth table for the combined premises.

The machine is a decided improvement over Jevons's. By abandoning the clumsy equational form which Jevons used, Marquand was able to cut down the number of keys to less than half of the 21 keys required on Jevons's model. In addition, the number of steps for feeding each premise to the machine is enormously reduced. A third advantage is that the simplified interior mechanism makes it possible to construct similar machines for more than four terms without enlarging the device to giant, unwieldy proportions. Charles Peirce, in an article on "Logical Machines" (*American Journal of Psychology*, Vol. 1, November, 1887, p. 165), summarizes these advantages in the following interesting and characteristic manner:

Mr. Marquand's machine is a vastly more clear-headed contrivance than that of Jevons. The nature of the problem has been grasped in a more masterly manner, and the directest possible means are chosen for the solution of it. In the machines actually constructed only four letters have been used, though there would have been no inconvenience in embracing six. Instead of using the cumbrous equations of Jevons, Mr. Marquand uses Professor Mitchell's method throughout.[1] There are virtually no keys except the eight for the letters and their negatives, for two keys used in the process of erasing, etc., should not count. Any number of keys may be put down together, in which case the corresponding letters are added, or they may be put down successively, in which case the corresponding combinations are multiplied. There is a sort of diagram face, showing the combinations or logical products as in Jevons's machine, but with the very important difference that the two dimensions of the plane are taken advantage of to arrange the combinations in such a way that the substance of the result is instantly seen. To work a simple syllogism, two pressures of the keys only are necessary, two keys being pressed each time. A cord has also to be pulled each time so as to actualize the statement which the pressure of the keys only formulates. This is good logic: philosophers are too apt to forget this cord to be pulled, this element of brute force in existence, and thus to regard the *solvet ambulando* as illogical. To work the syllogism with Mr. Jevons's machine requires ten successive movements, owing to the relatively clumsy manner in which the problem has been conceived.

Like Jevons's machine, Marquand's does not readily handle syllogisms involving "some" statements, but syllogisms with universal premises are taken care of easily. The premises of *Barbara*, for example—All *A* is *B*, All *B* is *C*—are fed to the machine in the negative form of:

$$Ab = 0$$
$$Bc = 0$$

The horizontal pointers then indicate the following four valid combinations:

$$ABC$$
$$aBC$$
$$abC$$
$$abc$$

If we examine the above combinations for the relation between A and C we find that only the combination of Ac does not appear. This tells us that "All A is C," the traditional conclusion of *Barbara*.

To illustrate how the machine handles the propositional calculus, Marquand cites two novel problems. Although he does not speak of them as examples of propositional logic, they are problems that today would be interpreted in truth-value rather than in class terms. They show that Marquand grasped much more clearly than did Jevons the ease with which propositional logic could be handled on a device of this type.

The first problem is stated by Marquand as follows:

Let us suppose that there are four girls at school, Anna, Bertha, Cora, and Dora, and that someone had observed that:
>   (1) Whenever either Anna or Bertha (or both) remained at home, Cora was at home; and
>   (2) When Bertha was out, Anna was out; and
>   (3) Whenever Cora was at home, Anna was at home.

What information is here conveyed concerning Dora?

To solve this problem we let A, B, C, D stand for the four girls, each letter corresponding to the initial of a girl's name. A capital letter indicates "at home" and a lower-case letter indicates the negative value of "not at home." (Since a girl must be either home or out, we have here two mutually exclusive values which permit us to put the problem into truth-value terms.)

The three premises, expressed by the symbols we have used in previous chapters, are:

1. $(A \vee B) \supset C$
2. $\sim B \supset \sim A$
3. $C \supset A$

Converting these to the required negative form and using Marquand's symbolism, we have:

1. $Ac = 0$
   $Bc = 0$
2. $bA = 0$
3. $Ca = 0$

When these four statements are fed to the machine, the face will appear as in Figure 85. An examination of the pointers, to determine what can be inferred about Dora, reveals that:

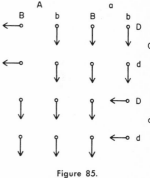

Figure 85.

D may combine with either *ABC* or *abc*.
d also may combine with either *ABC* or *abc*.

In other words, when Dora is at home the other three girls are either all at home or all out. And the same holds true when Dora is out.

Marquand's second problem is: if $A \equiv B$ and $B \equiv C$, what can be said of *D*? The first premise eliminates *Ab* and *aB* from the face of the machine; the second eliminates *Bc* and *bC*. Oddly enough, the face will then appear exactly as it did after impressing upon the machine the premises of the preceding problem (Figure 85). As Marquand puts it, the two problems seem to be quite different but actually describe the "same state of the logical universe." They are merely two ways of expressing an identical structure of relations involving four terms.

While preparing this chapter in 1956 I wrote to Princeton University in an effort to learn the present whereabouts of Marquand's historic machine, the first device of its kind to be constructed in the United States. No one in either the philosophy or psychology departments had the slightest notion of where it might be. An extensive search finally uncovered it in the stacks of the university library. It had been presented to the library several years earlier by Marquand's descendants, together with sixteen cartons of as yet unclassified scrapbooks, documents, and correspondence belonging to Marquand.

James Mark Baldwin, in an article on "Logical Machines" (in his *Dictionary of Philosophy and Psychology*, 1902) writes:

> In 1882 Marquand constructed from an ordinary hotel annunciator another machine in which all the combinations are visible at the outset, and the inconsistent combinations are concealed from view as the premises are impressed upon the keys. He also had designs made by means of which the same operations could be accomplished by means of electro-magnets.

Nothing whatever is known of the "hotel annunciator" machine, but a circuit design for its electromagnetically operated version was recently found among Marquand's papers by Professor Alonzo Church, of Princeton's mathematics department. (A photostat of Marquand's circuit diagram is reproduced in Wolfe Mays's article, "First Circuit for an Electrical Logic Machine," *Science*, Vol. 118, Sept. 4, 1953, p. 281; and the diagram has been analyzed in detail by George W. Patterson, Moore School of Electrical Engineering, University of Pennsylvania, in an unpublished paper, "A Nineteenth-century Electro-mechanical Logical Calculator.") This is probably the first circuit design ever drawn for an electrically operated logic machine, though there is no evidence that the machine was ever actually built. Dr. Mays gives 1885 as the probable date the design was drawn. The wiring diagram is of no special interest, since it merely provides an electrical method by which the keys of Marquand's machine can turn the pointers. Had small light bulbs been available at the time, Marquand would undoubtedly have used them instead of his electromagnetically operated pointers.

Mention also should be made of another logic device invented by Marquand and described in his article "A Machine for Producing Syllogistic Variations," Johns Hopkins University *Studies in Logic*, edited by Charles Peirce, 1883, p. 12. (A paper by Marquand on "The Logic of the Epicureans" also appears in this volume.) By turning a crank, the face of this machine exhibits in turn the eight different forms in which a syllogism can be expressed, assuming that each statement of the syllogism has two "contraposed" forms (e.g., "All *A* is *B*" or "All not-*B* is not-*A*"). The device would have delighted Ramon Lull, for it is merely an elaboration of his concentric rotating circles. By placing six rollers together in such a way that, when one was cranked, all of them would turn, the machine automatically runs through a Lullian table of exhaustive combinations for three statements, each of which is expressible in two forms. As Marquand points out, the same device can be used for other combinatorial purposes such as running through Jevons's logical alphabet for three terms.

The next advance in machines of the Jevons type seems to have been made by an Englishman named Charles P. R. Macaulay, about whom I have been able to learn nothing. In 1910, when he was living in Chicago, he applied for an American patent on a four-term logic machine. It was issued in 1913 as Patent 1,079,504 (obtainable for 25 cents from the U.S. Patent Office, Washington, D.C.). The machine combines, it seems to me, the best features of both Jevons's and Marquand's machines, with other features that make for an extremely compact and easily operated device. It is a small boxlike structure with three rows of windows through which various combinations of terms may be seen. Tilting the box in either of two directions causes interior rods to slide back and forth. Eight projecting pins on the left side of the box stand for the four terms and their negations. Pressing these pins causes the rods inside to lock in various positions so that, when the box is tilted, desired combinations can be brought into view. Consistent combinations appear in the upper row of windows, inconsistent combinations in the lower row. In the center row one can temporarily place combinations involved in particular ("some") propositions, a distinct improvement over both the Jevons and Marquand machines.

In his lengthy description of the machine, Macaulay explicitly points out its use for propositional logic. "The letters," he writes, "may be made to denote not only things, but also qualities, the truth of propositions, or any circumstances whatever." To illustrate, Macaulay poses the following problem: "Four hunters, *A, B, C* and *D*, occupied a camp in different ways for seven days. (1) On days when *A* hunted, *B* did not. (2) On days when *B* hunted, *D* also hunted, but *C* did not. (3) On days when *D* hunted, *A* or *B* hunted. How did they dispose themselves during the week? On how many days did *D* hunt and with whom?" As an interesting exercise, the reader may wish to solve this problem by Jevons's logical alphabet, or by one of the diagrammatic methods described earlier.

Although traditional syllogisms can be tested on machines of the Jevons type, the handling is, as we have seen, rather awkward. Since

Stanhope invented his demonstrator a number of other contrivances have been designed specifically for syllogisms, but none more fantastic than one developed by Annibale Pastore (b. 1868), professor of philosophy at the University of Genoa, Italy, and author of several books including one on *The Philosophy of Lenin*. The device, which strongly resembles a Rube Goldberg contraption, was constructed in 1903 with the aid of physics professor Antonio Garbasso. It is explained in preposterous detail in Pastore's work *Logica Formale, dedotta della considerazione di modelli meccanici (Formal Logic Deduced from the Consideration of Mechanical Models)*, published in Turin, 1906.[2]

Pastore's machine is an attempt to translate the structure of syllogistic reasoning into physical movement somewhat in the manner of an analogue computer. It consists essentially of a triangular arrangement of three groups of wheels representing the subject, predicate, and middle terms, and a complicated arrangement of differential gears, screws, weighted pendulums, and endless belts that join the wheels in a manner appropriate to the syllogism under consideration. Each group of wheels consists of one large wheel, representing "all" of its class, and two smaller wheels representing "some" of the same class. A universal affirmative proposition (All *A* is *B*) is indicated by running a belt from the large wheel of *A* to a small wheel of *B* so that, when *A* is turned, *B* will turn in the same direction. When two connected wheels rotate in opposite directions, a negative relation is indicated. Thus the universal negative (No *A* is *B*) is obtained by joining the large wheels of *A* and *B* with a belt that crosses itself between the wheels. An uncrossed belt joining two

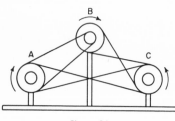

Figure 86.

small wheels is the particular positive (Some *A* is *B*) and a crossed belt from a small wheel to a large one is the particular negative (Some *A* is not *B*). Thus the syllogism: All *A* is *B*, No *B* is *C*, No *A* is *C*, would have belts connecting the wheels as shown in Figure 86.

If the belts represent a valid syllogism, cranking wheel *A* will cause all three wheels to rotate smoothly. If the wheels refuse to rotate, the syllogism is not valid. The device is designed primarily as a mechanical model of syllogistic inference rather than a machine for disclosing the valid conclusions of a given pair of premises.

To make the wheels respond properly to the structure indicated by the belts, a complicated arrangement of differential gears is necessary. For example, when a large wheel rotates, it must move the two smaller wheels on the same axle (since if all A is B, then some A must be B), but when a small wheel rotates, the large wheel must remain stationary (since if some A is B, we know nothing about all of A). But this is not all. To extend the power of the machine beyond the bounds of the traditional syllogism, Mr. Pastore added a second small wheel to each axle so that "some A is B" and "some A is not B" could be represented simultaneously by permitting the two small wheels of A to rotate in opposite directions while the large wheel remained motionless (since we know nothing about all of A).

A chart at the back of Pastore's book shows the belt connections for 256 possible combinations of syllogistic premises and conclusions. Of the 256, Pastore finds 32 valid syllogisms instead of the usual 24. This increased number is due to the fact that the machine recognizes as valid such syllogisms as: Some A is B, Some B is C, Some A is C, provided that the "some" is regarded as the *same* "some" in both premises. Of the 24 traditionally valid syllogisms, a few which require the assumption of non-empty classes are not validated by the machine.

As clumsy as Pastore's contrivance is, it does suggest that there are probably a wide variety of ways in which formal logic can be translated into simple mechanical phenomena.[3] There is no reason why, for example, rotating wheels cannot be used to express the propositional calculus. Each term would be represented by a wheel that rotated in one direction if the term were true, in the opposite direction if false. The relation of equivalence would be fed to the machine by setting gears so that, if either of two wheels were turned, the other wheel would turn in the same direction. "A implies B" would require that, when wheel A turned in a true direction, B would turn the same way, and when B turned in a false direction, A would turn likewise; but otherwise, turning either wheel would have no effect on the other. In similar fashion, the other binary relations could be expressed by suitable gear arrangements. If such a machine were fed a set of consistent premises, the wheels should all rotate in directions indicating the truth or falsity of the various terms. Indeterminate terms would be revealed by stationary wheels. Contradictions would result in locked wheels, and theorems would be disclosed by wheels that all rotated in a true direction only, regardless of which wheel was turned. Simple arithmetical calculating machines have been based on rotating disks (including one invented by Lord Stanhope), but whether this approach would result in a logic machine efficient enough to be of interest is an open question.

All the mechanical devices considered thus far, including Jevons's machine, are decidedly inferior in speed and power to the electric machines constructed in recent years. But before turning to this last and most exciting phase of our history, it remains to glance briefly at a grid principle by which cards can be superimposed to arrive at solutions of elementary logic problems.

References

1. The Mitchell to whom Peirce refers is one of his students, Prof. O. H. Mitchell, whose influential paper "On a New Algebra of Logic" appeared in the Johns Hopkins University *Studies in Logic,* edited by Peirce in 1883.

2. Pastore's book is reviewed at length by André Lalande in Vol. 63, 1907, pp. 268 ff., of the *Revue philosophique de la France et de l'etranger.* Lalande is sharply critical of Pastore's confused belief that his machine provides a genuine "experimental" approach to formal logic.

3. There is a sense in which all mechanical phenomena are expressive of logical relations. A lever with a fulcrum at one end will lift a weight at its center "if and only if" the other end is raised. But if the fulcrum is at the center, a weight on either end is raised only when the other end is lowered, a precise analogue of exclusive disjunction. A typewriter contains hundreds of working parts that can be considered expressions of "and," "or," "if, then," and other logical relations. This is what Peirce had in mind when he wrote, ". . . every machine is a reasoning machine, in so much as there are certain relations between its parts, which relations involve other relations that were not expressly intended. A piece of apparatus for performing a physical or chemical experiment is also a reasoning machine, with this difference, that it does not depend on the laws of the human mind, but on the objective reason embodied in the laws of nature. Accordingly, it is no figure of speech to say that the alembics and cucurbits of the chemist are instruments of thought, or logical machines." (Charles Peirce, "Logical Machines," *American Journal of Psychology,* Vol. 1, November, 1887).

7: Window Cards

Both the Stanhope demonstrator and the Pastore machine operate along mechanical lines that are in some ways analogous to the formal structure of syllogistic inference. If one is unconcerned with such analogy, desiring only a device that will produce the required conclusion from any pair of premises, then it is possible to invent a wide variety of simple gadgets for such purpose. Perhaps the simplest is a set of cards, one for each possible premise, with openings or "windows" cut on the cards in such a way that, when one card is placed on top of another, the valid conclusion, if any, will be revealed through one of the windows. When I designed a set of such cards for my article on "Logic Machines" (*Scientific American*, March, 1952) I thought I was certainly the first person ever to waste time on such a curious project. Later I discovered that the idea was at least seventy years old! Jevons, in his *Studies in Deductive Logic*, Chapter XI, describes a set of syllogistic window cards invented by a Mr. Henry Cunynghame. These cards are reproduced in Figure 87.

The working of Cunynghame's cards is easily explained. The premises appear at the top of each card. Major premises (in classical logic the major premise relates the middle term M to the predicate P of the conclusion) are at the top of eight cards; minor premises (relating the middle term M to the subject S of the conclusion) are at the top of the remaining eight. If we pick any major card, place a minor card on top, then all valid conclusions (if any) will

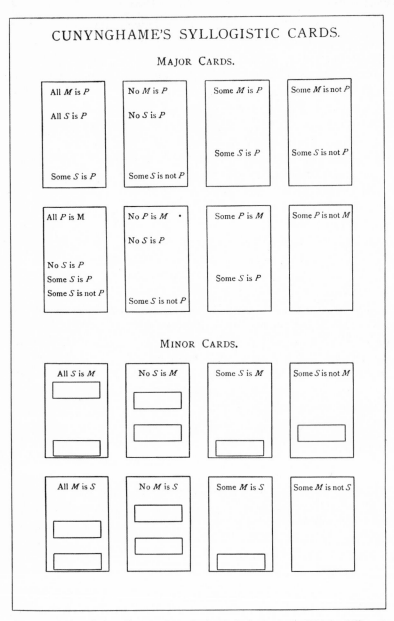

Figure 87. Grid cards for syllogisms. (From *Studies in Deductive Logic*, 1884, by William S. Jevons.)

appear in the window or windows of the upper card. Cunynghame applied the same principle to a metal device consisting of a hollow cylinder, with windows, that could be rotated around an inner solid cylinder. Jevons gives a brief description of it in the chapter just cited. A third device using the grid principle was presented by Cunynghame to the Science Museum, South Kensington, London, in 1885 but has not been on exhibition there for many years. This is simply a flat projection of the cylindrical model; a kind of circular slide rule. One cardboard disk, with slotted windows, turns upon a larger cardboard disk. Major premises appear on the circumference of the larger circle, minor premises on the circumference of the smaller one. When two premises are brought together, the conclusions, if any, appear in the openings below the minor premise. In a sense, it is a Lullian device, for the circles provide all possible combinations of premises with the additional feature of pointing out which combinations yield valid conclusions and what those conclusions are.[1]

None of these variations, however, exhibits in its construction or operation anything that resembles the formal structure of class logic. If you arbitrarily assume that certain invalid syllogisms are valid, and certain valid ones not, only a few alterations in the devices are necessary in order to obtain the new answers as readily as the old. For this reason, they have less logical interest than devices which may be clumsier to use, but which operate by principles analogous to the structure they are designed to analyze.

My set of cards for the *Scientific American* article is reproduced in Figure 88. In some respects these cards are simpler than Cunynghame's, in other ways more elaborate. Since the statement "No *A* is *B*" means the same thing as "No *B* is *A*," and similarly, "Some *A* is *B*" is the same as "Some *B* is *A*," I combined these equivalent statements on the same card. (Of course Cunynghame could have done the same, thus reducing the number of his cards from sixteen to twelve.) By adding an additional "conclusion card" with four windows for the four possible conclusions, I was able to prepare the premise cards so that it does not matter which card is put on top of the other. The two cards are simply placed together, the conclusion card put on top, and any window that shows solid black indicates a valid conclusion.

To make this clearer, suppose we wish to determine if the fol-

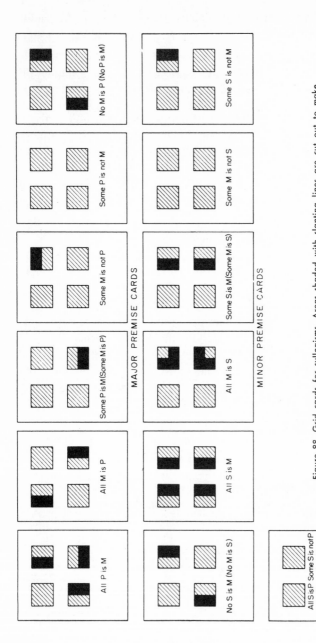

Figure 88. Grid cards for syllogisms. Areas shaded with slanting lines are cut out to make openings. (From Scientific American, March, 1952.)

lowing syllogism, voiced by the Patchwork Girl in L. Frank Baum's *The Lost Princess of Oz*, is valid:

> Somebody in Oz stole Ozma.
> Only wicked people steal.
> Therefore, someone in Oz is wicked.

We can state the conclusion more formally as "Some of the people in Oz are wicked people." "People in Oz" is therefore our subject (S), and "wicked people" the predicate (P). The premise containing P is traditionally regarded as the major premise. In this case it can be stated, "All people who steal are wicked people." The minor premise, containing S, may be phrased, "Some of the people in Oz are people who steal."

Our syllogism is, therefore, of the mood *IAI* (*Dimaris*) in the first figure:

> All M is P
> Some S is M
> Some S is P

To test this, we find the two premise cards and place them together, either above the other. When we cover them with the conclusion card we find that the window for "Some S is P" is solid black. This confirms the syllogism and indicates that the Patchwork Girl was not so scatterbrained as her behavior and conversation often suggested.

A more elaborate set of syllogism cards is pictured in Figure 89. To test a syllogism with them, pick out the desired major-premise card, put on top of it the desired minor-premise card, and on top of both, the desired conclusion card. If the syllogism is valid, the letter "T" will appear in one of the windows. If the syllogism is invalid, whatever formal fallacies are involved will appear along the right margin of the cards.

Grid cards can also be designed to operate on the same basis as the Venn diagrams (or Jevons's logical alphabet). They are awkward to use on syllogisms, but work fairly well with elementary problems in the propositional or truth-value calculus. If there are more than three terms, however, the number of cards required is so large that they serve no useful purpose.

Figure 90 shows a set of triangular-shaped cards of this type for

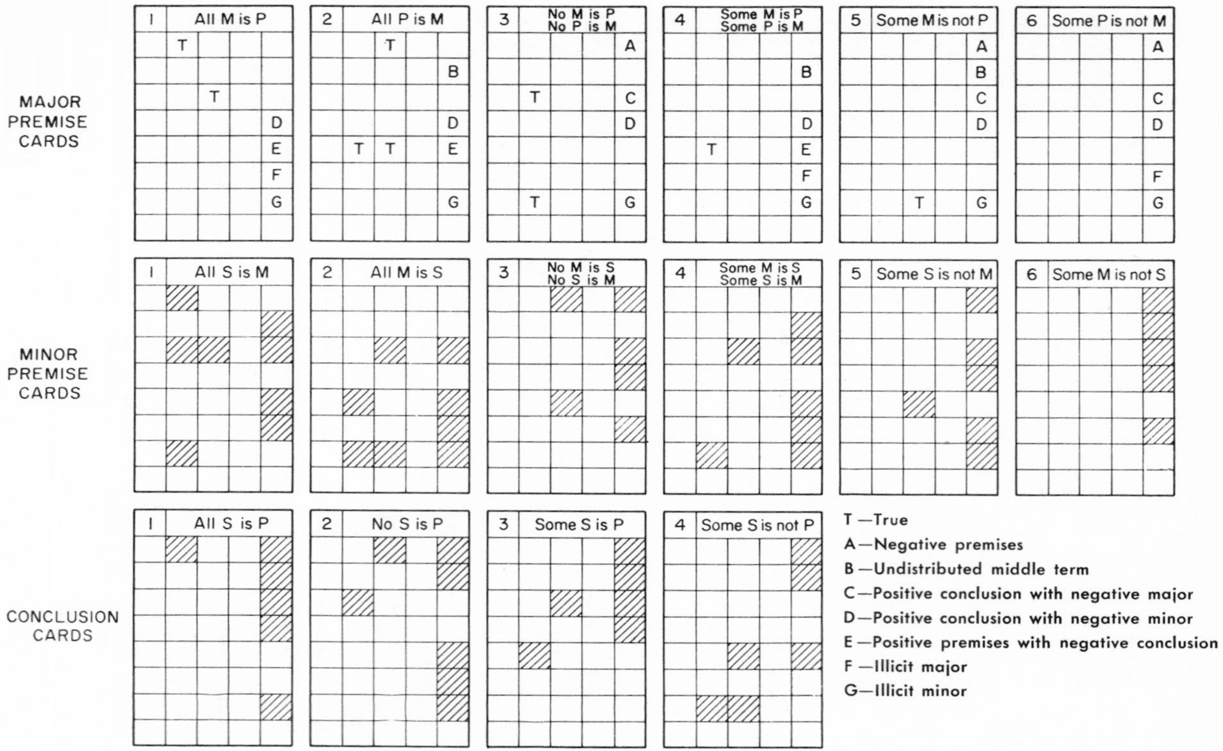
MAJOR PREMISE CARDS
1 All M is P
2 All P is M
3 No M is P No P is M
4 Some M is P Some P is M
5 Some M is not P
6 Some P is not M
MINOR PREMISE CARDS
1 All S is M
2 All M is S
3 No M is S No S is M
4 Some M is S Some S is M
5 Some S is not M
6 Some M is not S
CONCLUSION CARDS
1 All S is P
2 No S is P
3 Some S is P
4 Some S is not P
T—True
A—Negative premises
B—Undistributed middle term
C—Positive conclusion with negative major
D—Positive conclusion with negative minor
E—Positive premises with negative conclusion
F—Illicit major
G—Illicit minor

Figure 89. Grid cards that disclose formal fallacies of invalid syllogisms. Shaded areas cut out.

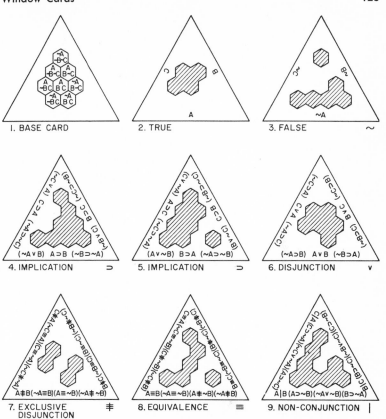

Figure 90. Triangular grid cards for propositional logic. Shaded areas are cut out.

handling up to three terms in the propositional calculus. Premises must be no more complicated than a binary relation or the assertion of truth or falsity for a single term. Only nine cards are shown in the illustration, but you should have on hand several duplicates of each card except the first one, since the same card may be required for more than one premise.

Cards 2 and 3 assert the truth value of a single term. Cards 4 through 9 are for binary relations. The basic form of the relation is shown on the edge, with less commonly encountered equivalent statements lettered on the same edge inside of parentheses. To solve a problem, pick out the required card for each premise, turning the card so that the premise appears on the bottom edge or base of the triangle. After all the premises have been assembled (it does not matter in what order), place them on top of card 1. Combinations visible through the windows are combinations consistent with the premises. Inspecting them will tell you what can be inferred about the terms.

A sample problem should make this procedure clear. Suppose we wish to determine, if possible, the truth values of B and C from the following premises:

> A is true (A)
> If B is true, then A is false ($B \supset \sim A$)
> Either B or C or both are true ($B \vee C$)

These premises are found on cards 2, 6, 9. We turn each card until the desired statement is at the bottom, then place all three cards on card 1. Only a single combination, $A \sim BC$, is visible through the grid. We therefore infer that B is false and C is true.

When no combinations at all are visible through the windows it indicates that at least two premises are contradictory. The entire procedure corresponds exactly to Jevons's elimination method and to the use of Venn circles for truth-value problems. Discussions of these procedures in Chapters 2 and 3 may be reviewed for additional details on how to handle the triangular cards.

Window cards have little value except as novelties, although they suggest how easily a punch-card machine could be devised that would take care of more complicated problems of formal logic with considerable efficiency. The most promising line of development, however, is offered by the recent electric network machines which provide the subject matter of the next chapter.

References

1. It was probably a circular device of this type that was constructed some time before 1935 by the well-known American psychologist Clark L. Hull. In his article on "The Mechanism of the Assembly of Behavior Segments in Novel Combinations Suitable for Problem Solution," *Psychological Review,* Vol. 42, May, 1935, p. 219, he writes that he once constructed a "simple mechanism of sliding disk-segments of sheet-metal which will solve automatically, i.e., exhibit the conclusions logically flowing from all of the known syllogisms and which will automatically detect all of the formal fallacies." Hull adds that he has not yet published a description of the device. I have been unsuccessful in attempts to learn more about its construction.

8: Electrical Logic Machines

If solving problems in formal logic were as important to society as solving problems in arithmetic, we would long ago have developed models of logic machines as compact as the Comptometer and the electrical adding machine. Unfortunately, problems in formal logic, too difficult to be solved in the head, are seldom encountered in either everyday life or the world of business. As a consequence, the construction of logic machines has been largely a recreational task. The Stanhope demonstrator, the Pastore device, even machines of the Jevons type must be regarded as crude first attempts, analogous to Napier's bones and the early arithmetical machines of Leibnitz, Pascal, and Babbage. At present, logic machines that operate by electric relays or electronic switching elements offer the most promising future, but even in this domain current research is still in a crude beginning phase.

Who was the first to build an electrical logic machine? As we have seen, Allan Marquand, in about 1885, saw the value of operating his logic machine electrically and even drew a circuit pattern for it, but there is no evidence that this version of his device was ever actually constructed. As far as I have been able to discover, the first man actually to build an electrical logic machine was Benjamin Burack, of the department of psychology, Roosevelt College, Chicago. His article on "An Electrical Logic Machine," *Science*, Vol. 109, June 17, 1949, p. 610, was the first published description of the device, although the machine was built and demonstrated as early as 1936.

Burack's machine is designed to test all syllogisms, including hypothetical and disjunctive forms, and also to test the conversion and obversion of propositions. To facilitate carrying, it was constructed inside a small suitcase (Figure 91). The lower part of this

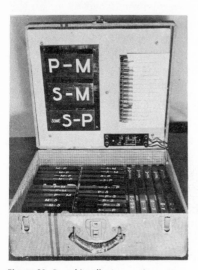

case contains thin plywood blocks lettered to represent various class propositions. To test a syllogism, the three required blocks are selected and placed in three spaces on the left side of the panel that fills the upper half of the suitcase. Metal contact areas on the backs of the blocks establish electrical connections between contact points on the panel so that, if the syllogism is invalid, one or more bulbs light up on the right side of the panel. The bulbs are labeled to indicate seven basic fallacies of the categorical syllogism, three fallacies for the hypothetical, one for the disjunctive, one for false conversion, and one for false obversion. An additional bulb indicates that the electric current (either battery or line) has been established.

Figure 91. Burack's syllogism machine. (Courtesy of Benjamin Burack.)

Since Burack first exhibited his machine, so many other types of electrical syllogism machines have been built, most of them by university students interested in logic and cybernetics, that it would be a difficult task to gather details about even a small portion of them. It is even possible to build a simple syllogism machine with the parts of a Geniac kit—an electrical brain construction kit currently sold by Berkeley Enterprises, Inc.[1]

None of these syllogism machines has a network that corresponds in any formal way with the structure of class logic. They are like the window cards of the previous chapter, using electrical connections, instead of the presence or absence of openings, to screen off invalid conclusions and transmit valid ones. When, however, we turn to the electrical machines that have been designed for the propositional calculus we enter an altogether different domain.

Here we find a striking analogy between the wire networks and the formal structure of the logic that the networks manipulate.

The close correspondence between electrical network theory and the propositional calculus seems to have dawned on many minds independently.[2] In the United States the first published paper on the topic was the historic article, "A Symbolic Analysis of Relay and Switching Circuits," by Claude E. Shannon, now a staff member of the electronics research laboratory, Massachusetts Institute of Technology. Based on the author's 1937 Master of Science thesis at M.I.T., it appeared in December, 1938, in the *Transactions of the American Institute of Electrical Engineers*, Vol. 57, p. 713. In this paper Shannon first explains how relay and switching circuits can be expressed by equations. The calculus for manipulating these equations is then shown to be isomorphic with the propositional calculus of symbolic logic. The values of true and false correspond to the open and closed states of a circuit; disjunction ("or") is indicated by series connections, and equivalence ("if and only if") by two circuits that open and close together.

Shannon's paper laid the groundwork for the construction of truth-value logic machines and also suggested new methods by which circuits could be designed and simplified. An unnecessarily complex circuit can be translated into the propositional calculus, the statement "minimized" (reduced to simplest form), then translated back to circuit design. Or a new circuit can be devised by stating the desired characteristics in the simplest possible logical form, then converting the statement to a circuit design. Shannon's paper also cast light on the logical aspects of computer programming. Giving orders to a giant brain, telling it to perform certain steps under certain circumstances, is more a logical than arithmetical matter, and the new electronic computers are being constructed with more and more attention paid to special circuits designed specifically to handle the logical aspects of the computer's work.[3]

Since Shannon's article appeared, rapid advances have been made in the application of symbolic logic to circuit theory, and scores of important papers on this topic have been published in engineering journals. Once again in the history of science a subject of seemingly academic interest only, pursued entirely for its own sake, suddenly turns out to have enormous practical value. As we move into the

new industrial age of electronic automation, there is every reason
to believe that the dull, detailed work of the symbolic logicians will
assume increasing practical importance in the designing of efficient
circuits for the more complicated automata.

It is possible to adjust a general-purpose digital computer so that
it can solve problems in the propositional calculus. It also is possible
to alter or add to the circuits of other types of computers so that
they can do the same. But numerical computers of all types, from
office adding machines to the giant brains, are not designed for handling formal logic and cannot be expected to operate as efficiently
in this area as a computer constructed specifically for a logical calculus.

The first electrical machine designed solely for propositional
logic was built in 1947 by two undergraduates at Harvard, William
Burkhart and Theodore A. Kalin. They had been taking a course in
symbolic logic with Professor Willard V. Quine and they had
chanced upon Shannon's paper on the relation of such logic to
switching circuits. Weary of solving problems by laborious paper
and pencil methods, and unaware of any previous logic machines,
they decided to build themselves an electrical device that would
do their homework automatically. The result, at a cost of about
$150 for the materials, was a small machine—now known as the
Kalin-Burkhart machine—capable of handling problems involving up to twelve terms in the propositional calculus (Figure 92).
The machine was first described in Edmund C. Berkeley's
Giant Brains, 1949, from which the following brief account is
taken.

Premises are fed to the Kalin-Burkhart machine by setting
switches which establish a circuit pattern isomorphic with the logical structure of the combined premises. The machine then scans the
entire truth table for this structure, taking the lines one at a time
at a rate of about one-half second per line. Each line is indicated on
the face of the machine by the pattern of lights in a row of twelve
red bulbs that correspond to the twelve terms. A glowing bulb indicates that the term is true. A yellow bulb lights whenever a row of
the truth table is valid, does not light when the row is false. Thus
by watching the machine and stopping it whenever a truth-table line
is valid, one can copy down the pattern of true and false terms as
indicated by the twelve red bulbs. The machine can also be set to

Figure 92. The Kalin-Burkhart machine, front and rear views. (Courtesy of William Burkhart.)

stop automatically when the yellow light is on, but must be started again manually.

At present the machine is in the possession of Burkhart, a member of the staff of Arthur D. Little, Inc., a research organization in Cambridge, Mass. (Kalin is now chief of the computer laboratory,

Air Force Cambridge Research Center, Hanscom Field, Bedford, Mass.) Although the machine is of great historic interest, marking a major turning point in the development of logic machines, so far no one has been able to find the slightest practical use for it. It can of course be used for solving problems of circuit theory, but unfortunately by the time such a problem has been translated into a form the machine can handle, and the answer translated back into circuit theory, the same problem can be solved by pencil and paper. It is interesting to note that when certain types of paradoxes are fed to the Kalin-Burkhart machine it goes into an oscillating phase, switching rapidly back and forth from true to false. In a letter to Burkhart in 1947 Kalin described one such example and concluded, "This may be a version of Russell's paradox. Anyway, it makes a hell of a racket."

It should be apparent to the reader that the Kalin-Burkhart machine is in a sense simply an electrical version of Jevons's logical piano. Its great superiority over Jevons's device is its power to handle many more terms, a power derived chiefly from the fact that instead of showing valid lines of a truth table simultaneously (creating an enormous space problem if many terms are involved) it takes the lines in a serial time sequence. This also may be considered a weakness in the machine, for it requires an operator to copy down the lines as they appear. This could be easily overcome, however, by adding to the machine an automatic recording mechanism.

The first electrical logic machine built in England, the Ferranti logical computer, was one that handled three terms only in the propositional calculus. Like the Kalin-Burkhart computer it operated by producing truth tables although its construction, in 1949, was on a different basis and made without knowledge of the work of Burkhart and Kalin. The Ferranti machine was jointly devised by Dr. Wolfe Mays, senior lecturer in philosophy at the University of Manchester, where Jevons himself had once taught, and D. G. Prinz of Ferranti, Ltd., Manchester. It was first described in a brief paper by Mays and Prinz, "A Relay Machine for the Demonstration of Symbolic Logic," *Nature*, Vol. 165, Feb. 4, 1950, p. 197. Plans for a more elaborate multivariable machine were announced by Dr. Mays ("Note on the Exhibition of Logical Machines," *Mind*, Vol. 60, April, 1951, p. 262) but the machine was never completed.

Since 1949 scores of other electrical logic machines have been built in various parts of the world, only a few of which have been announced or described in journals. The following is a partial list of references in English to some of these machines.

1. A three-term electronic device built at the National Physical Laboratory, Pretoria, South Africa, that exhibits its solutions on an oscilloscope screen. ("Venn Diagram Analogue Computer," by A. Archer, *Nature*, Vol. 166, Nov. 11, 1950, and his article of the same title, *South African Journal of Science*, Vol. 47, 1950, p. 133.)

2. A seven-term machine built in 1950 at the Edinburgh laboratory of Ferranti, Ltd., along lines similar to the Kalin-Burkhart computer, though constructed like the previous Ferranti machine without knowledge of the earlier American device. Pressing a button labeled "Think" starts the machine scanning a truth table for the combined premises fed to the machine. The machine stops on all "true" lines to permit copying, then starts scanning again when the "Think" button is pressed. ("Mechanized Reasoning. Logical Computers and Their Design," by D. M. McCallum and J. B. Smith, *Electronic Engineering*, Vol. 23, April, 1951).

3. A four-term machine built in 1951 by Robert W. Marks, New York, N.Y., and first announced in my article, "Logic Machines," *Scientific American*, March, 1952. To add a touch of whimsy, Marks attached a wire recorder and loud-speaker to his device so that it delivered its answers in a deep, impressive voice. For example, if a tested theorem proved to be false, the machine would say, "My name is Leibnitz Boole De Morgan Quine. I am nothing but a complicated and slightly neurotic robot, but it gives me great pleasure to announce that your statement is absolutely false."

4. A "feedback logical computer" for four terms. By using a feedback principle the machine is able to scan a problem in such a way that it can find *one* answer (that is, one "true" line of a combined truth table) without running through an entire truth table until it encounters one. If all possible answers are desired, the principle is of no value, but there are certain complex problems in which only a single answer is demanded. In such cases the machine cuts down the scanning time required to find this answer. The device was built in 1951 at the Edinburgh laboratory of Ferranti, Ltd.

("Feedback Logical Computers," by D. M. McCallum and J. B. Smith, *Electronic Engineering*, Vol. 23, December, 1951.)

5. A ten-term "truth-function evaluator" constructed at the Burroughs Research Center, Paoli, Pa. It employs a logical notation proposed by Jan Lukasiewicz in which all parentheses are eliminated by placing the variables and connectives in order from left to right according to the conventions of the notation. This has certain mechanical advantages. It is interesting to note that the idea of using the Lukasiewicz notation had occurred to Kalin as early as 1947. In a letter to Burkhart, Aug. 13, 1947, he discussed this at some length, expressing his opinion that "if there's ever a market for logic machines, I'll bet this is the most practical way to set up any useful (i.e., complicated) problem." ("An Analysis of a Logical Machine Using Parenthesis-free Notation," by Arthur W. Burks, Don W. Warren, and Jesse B. Wright, *Mathematical Tables and other Aids to Computation*, Vol. 8, April, 1954, p. 53; reviewed in *Journal of Symbolic Logic*, Vol. 20, March, 1956, p. 70. See also William Miehle's paper, "Burroughs Truth Function Evaluator," *Journal of the Association for Computing Machinery*, Vol. 4, April, 1957, p. 189.) The machine is pictured in Figures 93 and 94.

6. A five-term machine constructed in 1954 by Roger W. Holmes, professor of philosophy at Mt. Holyoke College, South Hadley, Mass. (Associated Press photograph and caption, distributed to papers of Mar. 8, 1954.)

All the above-mentioned machines are designed, I believe, to run through truth tables. In the testing of theorems, with which so much of modern logic is concerned, complete truth tables are essential, but if a machine is built primarily for solving problems in which one wishes to know what truth values for individual terms are uniquely determined by a given set of statements, it should be possible to construct a machine that dispenses entirely with the process of scanning truth tables. It is true that truth tables can be scanned very quickly if only a few terms are involved, but as the number of terms increases, the scanning time increases at an accelerating rate. Fifty terms, for example, present such a vast number of possible combinations that even the fastest modern electronic methods would be unable to cope with them in a reasonable length of time. It seems likely, therefore, that logic machines will be constructed some day on a basis that will eliminate the scanning procedure. Such ma-

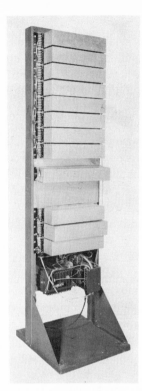

Figure 93. Front and back views of the Burroughs truth-function evaluator. (Courtesy of Burroughs Corporation.)

Figure 94. Control panel of the Burroughs truth-function evaluator. (From the *Journal of the Association for Computing Machinery*, April, 1957.)

chines would show instantly, after each new statement is fed to
them, the exact status of every variable. For example, each term
would have, say, a red bulb for true, a green bulb for false. If the
premises are consistent only with the truth of A, the falsity of B, but
do not determine the values of C and D, the machine would show a
red light for A, green for B, but no lights for C and D. Contradictions would be revealed by the simultaneous lighting of a term's red
and green bulbs. It might even be possible to construct such a device
without the use of expensive magnetic relays or electronic devices.
Although such a machine would be clumsy to use for testing theorems, it would solve certain types of logical problems with greater
speed than any of the present machines that operate on a scanning
basis.

It was mentioned earlier that a general-purpose digital computer,
constructed for numerical calculations, can also be used for solving
problems in the propositional logic. To do this it is first necessary
to assign binary numbers to the various truth functions. This is done
as follows:

We begin by constructing a table that will show the four possible
true-false combinations for two terms, A and B, using 1 for true, 0
for false. The left-to-right order in which the combinations appear
is arbitrary. Let us assume that the following order is adopted:

A	0	1	0	1
B	0	0	1	1

The relation of equivalence can now be represented by the following "designation number": 1001. This number simply tells us
that the first and fourth combinations in the above table (i.e., false-
false and true-true) are "true," whereas the other two combinations
(true-false and false-true) are "false." (The digits in the designation number correspond of course to the presence or absence of
shuttle lines in the network diagram explained in Chapter 3.) In a
similar manner we can arrive at a designation number for the other
binary functions:

$$A \vee B = 0 \ 1 \ 1 \ 1$$
$$A \equiv B = 0 \ 1 \ 1 \ 0$$
$$A \mid B = 1 \ 1 \ 1 \ 0$$
$$A \supset B = 1 \ 0 \ 1 \ 1$$
$$B \supset A = 1 \ 1 \ 0 \ 1$$

It is now possible to adjust the digital computer so that, when it is fed a series of premises that are expressed in binary numbers, it will combine these numbers and arrive at a designation number that expresses the combined premises. The "ones" in this final designation number will then tell us what lines of the final truth table are valid. In this way we can easily determine what can be inferred as to the truth or falsity of the individual terms. In fact the first Ferranti machine, designed by D. G. Prinz, operated precisely this way, handling three-term problems in just the way they would be handled by a large digital computer.

To make the process a bit clearer, suppose we wish the computer to give us the negation of a designation number. The machine has only to replace each 1 in the number by a 0 and each 0 by a 1. Thus the negation of equivalence (1001) would be 0110, which proves to be the designation number for the exclusive "or." (This process is analogous to the method of negating a function in the network diagram by removing all shuttles and drawing in the missing ones.)

If we wish the machine to give us a designation number for two functions connected by "and," it does so simply by multiplying the corresponding pairs of digits. For example: consider the following two premises:

> If and only if A is true, B is true.
> A is true.

What can we say about B?

As we have seen, the designation number for the first premise, which states the equivalence of A and B, is 1001. The designation number for the second statement is simply the binary number we originally assigned to A, namely, 0101. If we now multiply the corresponding pairs of digits we obtain 0001 as the designation number for the combined premises. This number tells us that only the last combination of the original truth table is true. Referring to the original table we see that in this last combination B is 1; therefore we know that B must be true.

What we are doing, of course, is simply performing in a notational way the elimination steps that we perform when we use the Venn diagrams for the propositional calculus, or Jevons's logic machine. If our premises contain a contradiction, our final designation number will consist entirely of zeros, just as all the compartments become shaded in the Venn system or all combinations vanish from the face of Jevons's machine. If the final designation number consists entirely of ones, it indicates that all lines of the final truth table are true. In other words, the statements fed to the machine constitute a law or theorem that holds regardless of how its terms vary in their truth or falsity.

The binary method can of course be extended to any number of terms, each additional term doubling the number of digits required in the basic designation numbers. Thus if we are working with three terms we must assign an eight-digit binary number to each term to represent an eight-line truth table:

A	0	1	0	1	0	1	0	1
B	0	0	1	1	0	0	1	1
C	0	0	0	0	1	1	1	1

Each binary function will also be an eight-digit number. For example, equivalence of B and C would in this case be expressed as 11000011. Premises are combined by multiplying as previously explained to obtain a final designation number which can be checked against the original table to determine what can be deduced about the truth or falsity of individual terms.

If binary relations are linked by other functions than "and," then other simple arithmetical rules will take care of them. The inclusive "or" of disjunction is handled as ordinary addition except that when 1 is added to 1 the sum is also 1. The exclusive "or" is also handled by addition, but in this case 1 plus 1 always gives 0. Equivalence is handled like the exclusive "or" except that after the results are obtained they are negated by changing every 0 to 1 and every 1 to 0.

One example should be sufficient to make clear how these relations are handled. Suppose we wish to test the statement $(A \supset B)$ v $(B \supset A)$ to see if it is a tautology. The designation number for the first implication is 1011, for the second implication 1101. To connect them by the relation of inclusive disjunction we add the numbers according to the rule given above, arriving at a final designation number of 1111. This tells us that every combination (or "line" of the truth table) is true; hence the statement is a tautology.

Because the rules for handling propositional logic in this binary system are so elementary,[4] it is possible to adjust a general-purpose digital computer so it can handle the logic easily. However, to ask a giant computer to perform such trivial tasks is like asking an elephant to oblige you by picking up a toothpick. The giant brains have much more important tasks on their hands, not to mention the time it takes to set the machine properly for handling logical problems.

In discussing Jevons's logic machine in an earlier chapter we called attention to the annoying fact that it did not provide answers in the simplest, most economical form. This is true also of the electric machines. The "answer" is usually a group of true lines from a truth table which then call for considerable thought and calculation before one can arrive at a simplified, condensed statement of what the machine has discovered. For example, a machine may tell you that the following combinations for two terms are valid: $AB \lor {\sim}AB \lor A \sim B$. This disjunctive chain is identical with the simpler disjunctive statement $A \lor B$, but the machine is powerless to perform this reduction.

The task of "minimizing" a complex disjunctive statement is often an arduous one. There are algebraic ways of doing this as well as chart methods,[5] but if there are a large number of variables, all these procedures are tedious and time-consuming. The question arises: can a minimizing machine be designed to do this job automatically? Such a machine could be of great value in simplifying costly relay circuits. A complex circuit could be translated into logical terms, the logical statement minimized, then translated back again into a circuit pattern.

How efficient such machines can be made is still undecided, but there is no doubt that they can be built, for one has already been constructed. The inventor, Daniel Bobrow, was attending high school in the Bronx when he designed in 1952 what is probably the world's first minimizing machine. The project was suggested to him by William Burkhart, with whom he had become acquainted, and parts for the device were supplied by Edmund Berkeley, the machine's present owner. Bobrow's twelve-page privately printed description, "A Symbolic Logic Machine to Minimize Boolean Functions of Four Variables, and Application to Switching Circuits," 1952, remains the only description of the machine to date. Bobrow is now attending the Rensselaer Polytechnic Institute, Troy, N.Y., where his interest has shifted from formal logic to other topics. Nevertheless, his minimizing machine, limited though its powers are, may signal the opening of a new and important area in the field of logic computers.[6]

References

1. Berkeley Enterprises, Inc., 513 Sixth Ave., New York 11, N.Y., was organized in 1948 by Edmund C. Berkeley, author of *Giant Brains,* 1949, and *Automatic Computing Machinery,* 1956. Originally a consulting service, the firm now publishes a monthly magazine, *Computer and Automation,* gives courses by mail, sells construction kits for building robots and computing devices, and issues a wide variety of books and pamphlets on subjects relating to logic and cybernetics.

2. The analogy between switching circuits and the propositional calculus was suggested as early as 1910 by P. Erénfést in his review, in a Russian journal, of Couturat's *Algébra logiki.* Details were worked out in 1934–1935 by the Russian physicist V. I. Séstakov, but not published until 1941. Without knowledge of this work, the same views were set forth in 1936 in a Japanese journal by Akira Nakasima and Masao Hanzawa. See *Journal of Symbolic Logic,* Vol. 18, December, 1953, p. 345.

3. See Edmund C. Berkeley's article, "The Relations between Symbolic Logic and Large-scale Calculating Machines," *Science,* Vol. 112, Oct. 6, 1950, p. 395. The author takes as an example the problem of designing a machine for the extraction of square roots by means of an iterative formula, showing how logical problems arise in programming the orders such a machine must follow.

4. For more detailed explanations of the binary method of manipulating the propositional calculus see Chapter 15, "Machines for the Solution of Logical Problems," by D. G. Prinz and J. B. Smith, in the anthology *Faster Than Thought,* 1953, edited by B. V. Bowden; and the following two articles by Robert S. Ledley, of the Operations Research Office, Johns Hopkins University, "A Digitalization, Systematization and Formulation of the Theory and Methods of the Propositional Calculus," *National Bureau of Standards Report,* No. 3363, February, 1954, and "Mathematical Foundations and Computational Methods for a Digital Logic Machine," *Journal of the Operations Research Society of America,* Vol. 2, August, 1954, p. 249 (reviewed in *Journal of Symbolic Logic,* Vol. 20, June, 1955, p. 195).

   It is not known who was the first to work out this method of manipulating propositional logic with binary numbers. It seems to have occurred to a large number of computer experts at about the same time, both in the United States and abroad, many of whom considered it too unimportant to justify an article on the subject.

   It is possible of course to diagram this method along the network lines proposed in Chapter 3. You begin with all possible shuttle connections drawn on the graph, then eliminate shuttles according to rules that correspond to the arithmetical rules of the binary method. At the finish you are left with only the valid shuttles from which the truth and falsity of individual terms may be determined. Similar procedures can be applied to Venn diagrams and to Jevons's logical alphabet. The difficulties in diagraming this method are so formidable, however, that the diagram has little value.

5. For a widely used chart method, consult chap. V on "Minimizing Charts" in *Synthesis of Electronic Computing and Control Circuits* by the staff of the

Computation Laboratory, Vol. 27, *Annals of the Computation Laboratory of Harvard University.* The charts were worked out by Howard H. Aiken, professor of applied mathematics and director of the laboratory. They are closely related to a grid or window-card system proposed by Lynn H. Loomis, of Harvard's mathematics department, and an algebraic method developed by Kalin and Burkhart.

Two other chart systems also are in common use under the names of the Veitch chart and the Karnaugh map. (See "A Chart Method for Simplifying Truth Functions," by E. W. Veitch, *Association for Computing Machinery, Proceedings,* May 2, 3, 1952; and "The Map Method for Synthesis of Combinational Logic Circuits," M. Karnaugh, *American Institute of Electrical Engineers, Transactions,* Vol. 72, Part 1, November, 1953, p. 593.) The Karnaugh map, a refinement of the Veitch chart, comes the closest to being a diagrammatic technique. It has considerable pedagogic value and includes an ingenious three-dimensional extension in which a cubical chart is employed for handling six variables.

In circuit theory the minimizing problem is complicated by the fact that the definition of the "simplest" or "most economical" circuit varies with the types of components involved. It is true that a circuit can be devised for every logical statement, but minimizing the statement does not always yield the most economical circuit. Apparently various experts in the computing field are independently evolving their own algebraic and chart techniques for minimizing, all based on essentially the same procedure, but a fully satisfactory technique has not yet been worked out.

Recent papers on the topic include "Circuit Minimization," by Edward Samson and Burton Mills, *AFCRC Technical Report* 54–2 (a United States Air Force memorandum of April, 1954); "Simplest Normal Truth Functions," by Raymond J. Nelson, *Journal of Symbolic Logic,* Vol. 20, 1955, p. 105; and "A Way to Simplify Truth Functions," by W. V. Quine, *American Mathematical Monthly,* Vol. 62, 1955, p. 627.

For early attempts to tackle the minimizing problem, see the last chapter of John N. Keynes's *Studies and Exercises in Formal Logic,* fourth edition, 1906. Keynes gives several methods, including a system of "multiplying out" devised by W. E. Johnson and published as early as 1892.

6. A close relation to a logic minimizing machine is the "relay circuit analyzer" built by Claude E. Shannon and Edward F. Moore for the Bell Telephone Laboratories, Murray Hill, N.J. The machine verifies whether a circuit satisfies given logical specifications and also makes a systematic attempt to reduce the circuit to simplest form. Since the machine considers each switch in terms of open, closed, or "don't care" positions, it is capable of applying a three-valued logic to switching circuits. See "Machine Aid for Switching Circuit Design," by Shannon and Moore, *Proceedings of the Institute of Radio Engineers,* Vol. 41, October, 1953, p. 1348.

9:   The Future of Logic
Machines

The ease with which formal logics can be trans-
lated into electric circuits leaves little doubt that we are entering a
period in the history of logic that will witness a steady development
in the construction of more powerful and versatile electrically operated machines. This does not mean that the nonelectrical logic
device has reached any state of near perfection. The few that have
been constructed are obviously crude models, and there are probably all kinds of ways in which compact little logic machines, operating along mechanical lines, can be designed. But the power of
such devices is so limited that attempts to invent better ones will
likely be rare and undertaken only in a recreational spirit. The most
exciting, as well as the most potentially useful area of exploration
will undoubtedly be in the electrical and electronic direction.

Electrical syllogism machines are so easily constructed and their
uselessness so apparent that it is unlikely much thought will be given
to improving them. The few that have been built are almost devoid
of theoretical interest because their circuits bear no formal analogy
to the logical structure of the syllogism. For classroom purposes it
should be possible, however, to construct a class logic machine that
would have such formal analogy, and it is surprising that this has
not, to my knowledge, been attempted. Such a machine would not
be confined to the traditional S, M, P labels, with their limited premises and conclusions. It would take care of many more variables,

and these could be applied to the terms of any number of class-inclusion statements. When such statements were fed to the machine it would show at once all the valid inferences that could be drawn. Such a machine would have a network structure analogous to the topological properties of the Venn circles. There is of course such an analogy in the network of propositional calculus machines, since the underlying structure of class and propositional logic is the same; but the truth-value machines are not designed primarily for class logic and a great deal of awkward translation has to take place before such machines can handle even simple syllogisms with particular statements. It should not be difficult to construct electrical machines designed specifically for class logic, and perhaps capable (like the Stanhope demonstrator) of handling statements involving "most," as well as statements with numerical quantifiers.

In the field of the propositional calculus, a great deal of experimental work is now going on. We can reasonably expect that simpler, more efficient, more powerful machines of this type will be devised in the near future. Will such machines have any practical uses? D. G. Prinz and J. B. Smith (in their chapter on logic machines in the anthology *Faster Than Thought,* edited by B. V. Bowden, 1953) suggest the following areas in which logic computers may some day be put to use: checking the consistency of legal documents, rule books of various sorts, and political policy statements; checking signal operations at railway junctions; preparing complex time schedules for university classes, plane landings at an airport, and so on. The rapidly growing field of "operations research" is riddled with problems for which logic machines may prove helpful. Edmund C. Berkeley, in his description of the Kalin-Burkhart machine (*Giant Brains,* 1949, Chapter 9), gives a complicated problem involving insurance coverage and shows how quickly it can be solved on the machine. Although none of these areas has so far grown complex enough to justify the frequent use of logic calculators, it may be that the employment of such devices will come with increasing complexity and may even be a factor in making such an increase possible.

It is amusing to speculate on what might happen to speculative philosophy if progress in semantics should some day permit the symbolic codification of systems of metaphysics. Fed with the required axioms and factual data, a machine might then examine the system for inconsistencies, make new deductions, translate its verbal expressions into the expressions of another system, and so on. Whole new systems of philosophy and religion could be constructed merely by twiddling a few dials and letting the machine explore the implications of new combinations of axioms.

The vast domain of multivalued logics lies open to exploration by electrical machines. As yet I know of no attempt to build machines for such purposes, but there seems to be no reason why this cannot be done. The fact that electrical switching circuits are "two-valued" (on or off) is certainly not a prohibitive factor. Multivalued logics are all based on matrix tables and it is safe to say that circuits can be designed for taking care of any type of matrix logic, even when the circuits rely solely on two-valued switching connections. (An exciting possibility is the use of continuously variable voltage currents for multivalued machines.) Such logic machines would have even less practical use at present than the two-valued devices, but as tools for research in multivalued logics they might save the professors a vast amount of time-consuming paper work and lead to new discoveries in this fascinating, dimly understood realm.[1]

It may also prove possible to construct machines for a logic of strict implication along lines developed by C. I. Lewis and others; machines to operate in the areas of the functional calculi of first, second, and higher orders; and machines to handle various types of relational algebras. There is no reason why any formal logic that can be manipulated with symbols on paper cannot also be manipulated by properly designed electric circuits. Unfortunately, in the absence of practical applications for these higher and queerer logics, there will be little incentive for the construction of expensive machines to handle them. Here and there, however, they may challenge the inventiveness of electrical engineers with a special interest in logic, and the next few decades may see some brilliant creative work along these lines.

In handling the functional calculi it is true that we encounter a "decision problem" in establishing formulas, and Alonzo Church has shown that there is no mechanical procedure by which all formulas in such calculi can be proved. But there are solutions to the decision problem in various areas of the calculi, and even where no decision procedure is possible, a machine can still be useful in checking proofs obtained by other methods.

Is it possible to build a logic machine or program a digital computer to solve logic problems in areas where there either is no decision procedure, or the procedure is so complex and time-consuming that it is beyond the speed and capacity of present machines? The answer is certainly yes. A strenuous effort is now under way [2] to develop a complex information-processing system (called by its inventors the "logic-theory machine") capable of searching for proofs of logic theorems in a manner closely analogous to the way a human logician searches for such proofs, namely, by trial and error, intuition, and sheer luck. The machine starts with a few basic axioms in its memory, then tries to find a chain of theorems that will eventually include the theorem it is trying to prove. Various cues guide the machine along the most promising lines, and the machine also modifies its search in the light of its trial experiences.

Although the logic-theory machine has been worked out only for the propositional calculus (in which proofs can also be found by the exhaustive truth-table method) its general technique is applicable to logics in which no decision procedure is possible, as well as to the solving of all sorts of important problems in areas where a decision procedure is not yet known, or if known, is beyond the speed and power of today's machines (e.g., solving a difficult chess problem). The system does not guarantee that a proof will be found or a problem solved. But it does provide a technique that duplicates the human logician's ability to discover proofs and solve problems within a reasonable computing time in areas where exhaustive mechanical procedures are impossible, not known, or impractical to adopt. The system is designed for digital computers, and satisfactory empirical tests of it were made in 1956 with the Rand Corporation's computer Johnniac.

We have already mentioned the utility of the two-valued logic circuits in giving orders to giant mathematical calculators. Another practical application of logic circuits to giant brains of the future is in the wiring of mammoth memory machines for storing information in such a way that needed data can be obtained quickly and easily. In an article in the *Atlantic Monthly* ("As We May Think," July, 1945) Vannevar Bush, one of the pioneers of cybernetics, proposed what he termed a "Memex" machine. It would store huge amounts of information on microfilm or in electronic devices, elaborately cross-referencing the data by a process analogous to the way ideas are associated in the human brain. If asked a question about its data, a scanning system in the Memex would quickly print and deliver all the relevant information. Logical circuits would obviously play a large role in the construction of such a machine.[3]

It is surprising to learn that a machine of this type (including data recorded with probability values) was suggested as early as 1851 by a prominent British surgeon, Dr. Alfred Smee, in an odd little book called *The Process of Thought*. The doctor confessed, however, that the machine he had in mind would "cover an area exceeding probably all London." Modern electronic methods for storing information have, of course, made it possible to construct such machines on a much smaller scale than the doctor would have dared dream.

In his later years H. G. Wells became convinced that the accelerating complexity of science had created a problem of communication and storage of information that called for bold plans. There are now several thousand periodicals published in the United States dealing with biology alone. A scientist sometimes finds it faster and cheaper to investigate a problem all over again than to search this mountain of literature for records of previous research. In his book *World Brain,* 1938, Wells argues for a gigantic clearing-house into which all research reports would be channeled, and from which information would be distributed to all parties concerned. This "world brain" would keep data stored on microfilm and issue vast encyclopedias of the sciences that would be kept constantly up to date. It would be, Wells wrote, "a double-faced organization, a perpetual digest and conference on the one hand and a system of publication and distribution on the other. It would be a clearing house for universities and research institutions; it would play the role of a cerebral cortex to these essential ganglia."

Wells was writing before the development of cybernetics. Were he alive today he would undoubtedly be pressing demands for a "world brain" that would make use of electronic storage units and logical circuits for its Gargantuan task of collecting, collating, and distributing scientific information.

At present (1958) the Soviet Union has made greater strides than any other nation toward Wells's vision. According to *The New*

York Times, Nov. 25, 1957, Russia's All-Union Institute of Scientific and Technical Information issues thirty-six journals of scientific articles in translation, each journal appearing forty-eight times a year. Another Russian agency, the Institute of Scientific Information, publishes thirteen journals that summarize and index articles in about 8,000 periodicals from more than eighty countries, including 1,400 from the United States. Dr. D. R. Newth, a British zoologist, described this as the "really shattering thing" he saw on a recent trip to Russia. "No other agency in the world is doing this job," he declared. "I wish to God I could read Russian." (Quoted in Robert Wallace's article, "First Hard Facts on All Russian Sciences," *Life*, Dec. 16, 1957.)

By contrast, in 1957 only thirty of 1,200 Russian scientific journals received by the United States government were being translated and made available. A group of American industries, after spending $200,000 for five years of research on an electric circuit problem, discovered that the answers had been published in Russia before they had even started their work. A Soviet paper on hydrodynamics was secretly translated seven times by seven separate government agencies, each unaware of the other's effort. When Lloyd V. Berkner, president of a New York research organization, was asked by a Congressional committee to identify the agencies (*The New York Times*, Jan. 21, 1958) he stated that he was not free to do so because the mere fact that the agencies were translating Soviet papers was classified. There is reason to hope, however, that the Soviet Sputniks have prodded the nation into taking long overdue steps to remedy this appalling situation. The time is rapidly approaching when only electronic machines will be able to handle adequately the task of translating, summarizing, indexing, and issuing abstracts of this never-ending, constantly swelling flood of scientific information.

To logicians and mathematicians working in the field of inductive logic and probability theory, the possible use of calculating machines opens up still further vistas for the imagination. Can a machine be designed that will survey a number of observational reports and produce a reasonable hypothesis to explain them? Can a machine be designed that will take a given hypothesis, correlate it with all relevant observational data, and tell us the *degree* to which the hypothesis has been confirmed? At the moment no one has the slightest notion of how a machine could be constructed for either of these purposes. The invention of hypotheses, like the inventing of useful machines, is a mental process far from understood. It obviously involves a special kind of intuitive ingenuity to combine concepts in novel ways and to spot quickly the value of certain combinations. An element of luck is also often involved. Certainly there is no mechanical procedure by which creative work of this sort can be done. A crude Lullian device may be used, as explained in Chapter 1, to present the mind with novel combinations of ideas, but if any great scientist or inventor has ever found such a device useful, he has never publicly acknowledged it.

Nor is there any mechanical procedure for testing a hypothesis. We do not even have a way of assigning a numerical value or "weight" to a scientific theory. The most we can say of the general theory of relativity, for instance, is that it has been confirmed to a high degree. But exactly what do we mean by "high"? In this region science can only make statements comparable with statements made about heat in days before thermometers. Men were certain that fire was "hotter" than ice, or that the weather was "colder" in winter than summer, but when it came to deciding whether one summer day was hotter than another, there was room for argument. Progress in science has always depended on the quantification of data, the assigning of numbers to phenomena so that changes can be measured accurately and described by equations. It may be that scientific theories will never submit to measurement of this sort, but it would be rash to assume this. A great deal of abstruse technical work is currently being done on this problem. If inductive logic takes the shape of a workable calculus, even if only in restricted areas of science, there is a good chance that machines can be devised for handling it.

Rudolf Carnap, in his monumental *Logical Foundations of Probability,* 1950, takes this optimistic view. He points out that even in deductive logic there are only limited areas in which mechanical procedures are possible. For example, there is no procedure (hence no machine) that will discover fruitful or interesting new theorems in logic or mathematics. As in science, the ability to find such theorems rests upon intuition and luck. Again: there is no effective procedure (hence no machine) that will find a proof for a logical or mathematical theorem except on the lowest levels of logic, the truth-value calculi where the matrix method is applicable. It is possible, however, to find mechanical procedures for checking proofs in the higher logics, and Carnap believes that corresponding procedures can be found in inductive logic for determining the degree of confirmation of a working hypothesis once it has been formulated. He gives as a trivial example the fact that there are three million people in Chicago of whom two million have dark hair. We wish to determine the color of hair of an individual. All we know about him is that he lives in Chicago. We conclude, therefore, that the hypothesis that the individual has black hair has a degree of two-thirds confirmation. In brief, a logic of probability underlies inductive reasoning, and to the degree that such reasoning employs this logic, to that degree will it be possible to devise machines for handling it.

> The . . . point has sometimes been formulated [Carnap writes, p. 193] by saying that it is not possible to construct an inductive machine. The latter is presumably meant as a mechanical contrivance which, when fed an observational report, would furnish a suitable hypothesis, just as a computing machine when supplied with two factors furnishes their product. I am completely in agreement that an inductive machine of *this* kind is not possible. However, I think we must be careful not to draw too far reaching negative consequences from this fact. I do not believe that this fact excludes the possibility of a system of inductive logic with exact rules or the possibility of an inductive machine with a different, more limited, aim. It seems to me that, in this respect, the situation in inductive logic is similar to that in deductive logic.[4]

The question of whether a machine can ever be devised that will perform the creative tasks of devising experiments, suggesting hypotheses, inventing useful machines, and so on, carries us into a realm where only philosophers and the writers of science fiction can profitably venture. From our present vantage point, the frontiers of science spread out in all directions into areas of seemingly infinite and unpredictable variety. If the whole of scientific knowledge rests ultimately on a set of principles that are finite in number, with all things taking their appointed places in a rigid deductive structure, and if all these basic principles became known, then the situation would be radically altered and machines for exploring the structure might become a possibility. This was, as we saw in the first chapter, the dream of Lull and Leibnitz; and even Francis Bacon, though he had only harsh words for Lull, also supposed that there was a final limit to scientific knowledge. Bacon's system of induction rests squarely on the possibility of obtaining an exhaustive list of facts relevant to a given inductive problem. Unfortunately, the universe seems to be vaster and more varied than Bacon imagined, thus rendering his system unworkable in its essential aspects. It is interesting to speculate on whether this will always be the case. If physics, for example, ever becomes a deductive system (as Eddington, Milne, and some other mathematical physicists have suggested it might), with a finite number of postulates, then the possibility returns of discovering a new law or inventing a new gadget in much the same way that a geometer proceeds to investigate the properties of a geometrical figure. As we have seen, however, even in mathematics the discovery of new theorems is more intuitive than mechanical. Add to this the upsetting discovery of Kurt Gödel, dashing the hopes that all mathematics can ever be caught in one deductive web, and the possibility of an inductive machine creative enough to replace the scientist becomes remote indeed.

All these topics have long been familiar to the writers of modern science fiction. I am not referring to the robots of science fantasy (artificial creatures, mechanical or otherwise), but to the mammoth electronic brains that lack powers of locomotion. Such brains often take over the functions of government, develop self-awareness, become psychotic, duplicate themselves, often outlast or destroy the race of creatures that originally constructed them. *Brain,* a three-act play by Lionel Britton (published in England in 1930) was one of the earliest fantasies, if not the first, to introduce a machine of this type—a "cold, dark, dead thing creeping over the world." All the knowledge of humanity was fed to the Brain, where it was combined with logical connectives so that the Brain could give objective, unemotional answers to all questions, including moral and political ones. Over the centuries it grew in power until it became the master of the race. Since Britton's play, giant brains of this sort have figured in hundreds of science fiction novels and short stories.

The fear that machines may develop creative powers and a will of their own has received classic literary treatment in Samuel Butler's *Erewhon,* Karel Capek's *R.U.R.,* and Ambrose Bierce's terrifying story of the robot chess player who strangles his inventor after losing a game. Charles Peirce did not share these fears. In his article "Logical Machines" (from which we quoted in Chapter 6) he argues that, even if a machine could be constructed with the power to "direct itself between different possible procedures" and so thread its way through complicated proofs,

. . . it would still remain true that the machine would be utterly devoid of original initiative, and would only do the special kind of thing it had been calculated to do.[5] This, however, is no defect in a machine; we do not want it to do its own business, but ours. The difficulty with the balloon, for instance, is that it has too much initiative, that it is not mechanical enough. We no more want an original machine, than a housebuilder would want an original journeyman, or an American board of college trustees would hire an original professor.

If Peirce were alive today, perhaps his optimism would be shattered by the many recent machines that are capable of learning from experience. W. Gray Walter's *docilis*, a mechanical "turtle," has no difficulty at all in developing conditioned reflexes. Claude Shannon's mouse is one of several ingenious mechanisms constructed for running mazes. The mouse first blunders his way through a maze until he solves it by trial and error; but he "remembers" all that he has learned about the maze so that when given a second trial he runs the maze without a single false turn. Machines of this sort can acquire unpredictable behavior patterns, and to the degree that they do, they cease in a sense to be obedient. They do what they have *learned* to do, an altogether different matter from what they are *wired* to do.

Or is it altogether different? The distinction begins to blur when we reflect on the sense in which even digital computers learn from experience. After reading an early draft of this chapter, William Burkhart wrote (and I quote with his permission):

In doing division a desk calculator subtracts until it gets a negative remainder, adds back until it gets a positive remainder, then shifts and repeats. Similarly, an electronic calculator decides what to do next on the basis of past results of computation. For example, in calculating a table of sines or cosines the machine will guess the first value poorly. But when it computes the next value in the table it will first guess that the answer is the same as the previous answer (a good guess) and go on from that point successively improving its approximations to any desired degree of accuracy. On each successive approximation the machine notes how close its answer is to the previous one. When, finally, two successive answers differ by a negligible amount, the calculator stops approximating and prints its answer.

Is such a machine, which slavishly follows rules, learning? I think not. Rather it is just another machine following rules slavishly. To learn, I believe we must generalize, and this is a creative process. Before building true learning machines we must first learn to build creative and inductive machines. . . .

Machines are things which manipulate symbols exactly as they are wired to do. If we interpret their inputs and outputs as being numbers, then the machine is a computer. If we interpret the answers as logical statements, it is a logic machine. If we connect the outputs to a motor, the machine is a modern elevator control system. If we connect them to a mechanical mouse, it is a parlor game. . . .

In most cases, one's attitude toward these vexing questions will depend on whether one is a philosophical mechanist, regarding man as nothing more than an extremely complicated symbol-manipulating and information-processing machine (doing what it is wired to do by heredity and wired to learn to do from its environment) or an idealist who believes man to be something more than this. To a large extent, this conflict may be a matter of words. William James, for example, believed that human personality was capable of surviving death, yet he regarded the human brain as a tool which learns in a manner analogous to the way an earthworm learns. Of course man's powers of learning and thinking are of a much higher order than the powers of an earthworm or Shannon's mechanical mouse, but it is hard to see where a line can be drawn on the evolutionary tree to separate one type of learning from another. There seems to be only a spectrum of increasing neural complexity, and as with all spectrums, one can talk about it in words that emphasize continuity and sameness of parts, or in words that emphasize distinctions and differences between the parts.

If the idealist will grant that man's ability to think creatively may arise from an extremely intricate, as yet unknown type of neural structure, the mechanist might be willing to concede that powers of symbol manipulation have emerged from this structure which are qualitatively different from those possessed by man-made machines or even by the lower animals. In the light of these concessions, the two attitudes may not be so far apart as the rhetoric usually employed by both sides would suggest.

In science fiction even the "dead," obedient logic machines have reached proportions awesome enough to stagger one's credulity. Clifford D. Simak's story, "Limiting Factor" (first published in *Startling Stories,* November, 1949) tells of a group of space explorers who come upon a small uninhabited planet completely surrounded by a shell of burnished metal. Below this shell, extending downward for twenty miles and all around the planet, is the interior of an electronic machine. Presumably the culture that had once flourished on the planet's natural surface, beneath the machine, had faced problems of such colossal magnitude that it had been forced to migrate to a larger planet where an even larger machine could be built.

A spoon slides from the knapsack of one of the spacemen as he leans over a ramp. It falls through a maze of circuits, tubes, wheels, shafts, and mysterious cubes of crystal; tinkling its way past the dusty parts of a mechanism so vast that the human race may never fathom how to use it or learn the purposes for which it was constructed.

References

1. See the *Journal of Symbolic Logic*, Vol. 22, March, 1957, p. 102, for brief reviews of the following two articles by Japanese engineers: "On the Representation of Finitely Many-valued Logics by Electric Circuits," by Toshihiko Kurihara, and "On the Representation of Many-valued Propositional Logics by Relay Circuits," by Kamenosuke Yasuura, both in the *Technology Reports of the Kyushu University,* Vol. 28, No. 2, 1955.

2. See "The Logic Theory Machine" by Allen Newell and Herbert A. Simon, Rand Corporation Report P-868, July 12, 1956, and Institute of Radio Engineers *Transactions on Information Theory*, Vol. IT-2, No. 3, September, 1956; "Empirical Explorations of the Logic Theory Machine" by Newell, J. C. Shaw, and Simon, Rand Corporation Report P-951, Jan. 11, 1957; and "Programming the Logic Theory Machine" by Newell and Shaw, Rand Corporation Report P-954, Jan. 11, 1957.

3. The analogy between electrical circuits and nets of nerve cells in the brain is so striking that the question immediately arises: is "thinking" a process involving actual circuits, switches, and scanning devices? Many important papers groping in this cloudy area have appeared. The interested reader should consult chap. XLVI on "Boolean Algebra of Neural Nets" in *Mathematical Biophysics* by Nicolas Rashevsky, revised 1948 edition (Rashevsky's earlier articles on the subject are given in a list of references at the end of the chapter); "A Logical Calculus of the Ideas Immanent in Nervous Activity," by Warren S. McCulloch and Walter Pitts, *Bulletin of Mathematical Biophysics,* Vol. 5, 1943, p. 115 (reviewed in the *Journal of Symbolic Logic,* 9, p. 49); and "The Brain as a Computing Mechanism," by McCulloch, *Electrical Engineering,* Vol. 68, 1949, p. 492.

4. Cf. pp. 197 and 206 of Carnap's book. On p. 297 a pair of diagrams illustrating the difference between deductive logic (topological and nonquantitative) and inductive logic (requiring numerical measurement) could be interpreted as illustrations of the two ways Lord Stanhope used his demonstrator —one for syllogisms and the other for what he called "The logic of probability" (see chap. 4). Actually, Stanhope's device is the first crude attempt at precisely the kind of "inductive machine" Carnap has in mind.

5. In L. Frank Baum's *The Road to Oz,* 1909, Tik-tok (a wind-up mechanical man who "thinks, speaks, acts, and does everything but live") is described as being popular with the citizens of Oz for precisely the qualities Peirce finds desirable in a logic machine. ". . . he was so trustworthy, reliable and true; he was sure to do exactly what he was wound up to do, at all times and in all circumstances. Perhaps it is better to be a machine that does its duty than a flesh-and-blood person who will not, for a dead truth is better than a live falsehood."

Index

CATALOGUE OF DOVER BOOKS

BOOKS EXPLAINING SCIENCE AND MATHEMATICS

General

WHAT IS SCIENCE?, Norman Campbell. This excellent introduction explains scientific method, role of mathematics, types of scientific laws. Contents: 2 aspects of science, science & nature, laws of science, discovery of laws, explanation of laws, measurement & numerical laws, applications of science. 192pp. 5⅜ x 8. S43 Paperbound **$1.25**

THE COMMON SENSE OF THE EXACT SCIENCES, W. K. Clifford. Introduction by James Newman, edited by Karl Pearson. For 70 years this has been a guide to classical scientific and mathematical thought. Explains with unusual clarity basic concepts, such as extension of meaning of symbols, characteristics of surface boundaries, properties of plane figures, vectors, Cartesian method of determining position, etc. Long preface by Bertrand Russell. Bibliography of Clifford. Corrected, 130 diagrams redrawn. 249pp. 5⅜ x 8. T61 Paperbound **$1.60**

SCIENCE THEORY AND MAN, Erwin Schrödinger. This is a complete and unabridged reissue of SCIENCE AND THE HUMAN TEMPERAMENT plus an additional essay: "What is an Elementary Particle?" Nobel laureate Schrödinger discusses such topics as nature of scientific method, the nature of science, chance and determinism, science and society, conceptual models for physical entities, elementary particles and wave mechanics. Presentation is popular and may be followed by most people with little or no scientific training. "Fine practical preparation for a time when laws of nature, human institutions . . . are undergoing a critical examination without parallel," Waldemar Kaempffert, N. Y. TIMES. 192pp. 5⅜ x 8. T428 Paperbound **$1.35**

FADS AND FALLACIES IN THE NAME OF SCIENCE, Martin Gardner. Examines various cults, quack systems, frauds, delusions which at various times have masqueraded as science. Accounts of hollow-earth fanatics like Symmes; Velikovsky and wandering planets; Hoerbiger; Bellamy and the theory of multiple moons; Charles Fort; dowsing, pseudoscientific methods for finding water, ores, oil. Sections on naturopathy, iridiagnosis, zone therapy, food fads, etc. Analytical accounts of Wilhelm Reich and orgone sex energy; L. Ron Hubbard and Dianetics; A. Korzybski and General Semantics; many others. Brought up to date to include Bridey Murphy, others. Not just a collection of anecdotes, but a fair, reasoned appraisal of eccentric theory. Formerly titled IN THE NAME OF SCIENCE. Preface. Index. x + 384pp. 5⅜ x 8. T394 Paperbound **$1.50**

A DOVER SCIENCE SAMPLER, edited by George Barkin. 64-page book, sturdily bound, containing excerpts from over 20 Dover books, explaining science. Edwin Hubble, George Sarton, Ernst Mach, A. d'Abro, Galileo, Newton, others, discussing island universes, scientific truth, biological phenomena, stability in bridges, etc. Copies limited; no more than 1 to a customer, FREE

POPULAR SCIENTIFIC LECTURES, Hermann von Helmholtz. Helmholtz was a superb expositor as well as a scientist of genius in many areas. The seven essays in this volume are models of clarity, and even today they rank among the best general descriptions of their subjects ever written. "The Physiological Causes of Harmony in Music" was the first significant physiological explanation of musical consonance and dissonance. Two essays, "On the Interaction of Natural Forces" and "On the Conservation of Force," were of great importance in the history of science, for they firmly established the principle of the conservation of energy. Other lectures include "On the Relation of Optics to Painting," "On Recent Progress in the Theory of Vision," "On Goethe's Scientific Researches," and "On the Origin and Significance of Geometrical Axioms." Selected and edited with an introduction by Professor Morris Kline. xii + 286pp. 5⅜ x 8½. T799 Paperbound **$1.45**

BOOKS EXPLAINING SCIENCE AND MATHEMATICS

Physics

CONCERNING THE NATURE OF THINGS, Sir William Bragg. Christmas lectures delivered at the Royal Society by Nobel laureate. Why a spinning ball travels in a curved track; how uranium is transmuted to lead, etc. Partial contents: atoms, gases, liquids, crystals, metals, etc. No scientific background needed; wonderful for intelligent child. 32pp. of photos, 57 figures. xii + 232pp. 5⅜ x 8. T31 Paperbound **$1.50**

THE RESTLESS UNIVERSE, Max Born. New enlarged version of this remarkably readable account by a Nobel laureate. Moving from sub-atomic particles to universe, the author explains in very simple terms the latest theories of wave mechanics. Partial contents: air and its relatives, electrons & ions, waves & particles, electronic structure of the atom, nuclear physics. Nearly 1000 illustrations, including 7 animated sequences. 325pp. 6 x 9. T412 Paperbound **$2.00**

Catalogue of Dover Books

THE STRANGE STORY OF THE QUANTUM, AN ACCOUNT FOR THE GENERAL READER OF THE GROWTH OF IDEAS UNDERLYING OUR PRESENT ATOMIC KNOWLEDGE, B. Hoffmann. Presents lucidly and expertly, with barest amount of mathematics, the problems and theories which led to modern quantum physics. Dr. Hoffmann begins with the closing years of the 19th century, when certain trifling discrepancies were noticed, and with illuminating analogies and examples takes you through the brilliant concepts of Planck, Einstein, Pauli, de Broglie, Bohr, Schroedinger, Heisenberg, Dirac, Sommerfeld, Feynman, etc. This edition includes a new, long postscript carrying the story through 1958. "Of the books attempting an account of the history and contents of our modern atomic physics which have come to my attention, this is the best," H. Margenau, Yale University, in "American Journal of Physics." 32 tables and line illustrations. Index. 275pp. 5⅜ x 8. T518 Paperbound **$1.75**

THE EVOLUTION OF SCIENTIFIC THOUGHT FROM NEWTON TO EINSTEIN, A. d'Abro. Einstein's special and general theories of relativity, with their historical implications, are analyzed in non-technical terms. Excellent accounts of the contributions of Newton, Riemann, Weyl, Planck, Eddington, Maxwell, Lorentz and others are treated in terms of space and time, equations of electromagnetics, finiteness of the universe, methodology of science. 21 diagrams. 482pp. 5⅜ x 8. T2 Paperound **$2.25**

THE RISE OF THE NEW PHYSICS, A. d'Abro. A half-million word exposition, formerly titled THE DECLINE OF MECHANISM, for readers not versed in higher mathematics. The only thorough explanation, in everyday language, of the central core of modern mathematical physical theory, treating both classical and modern theoretical physics, and presenting in terms almost anyone can understand the equivalent of 5 years of study of mathematical physics. Scientifically impeccable coverage of mathematical-physical thought from the Newtonian system up through the electronic theories of Dirac and Heisenberg and Fermi's statistics. Combines both history and exposition; provides a broad yet unified and detailed view, with constant comparison of classical and modern views on phenomena and theories. "A must for anyone doing serious study in the physical sciences," JOURNAL OF THE FRANKLIN INSTITUTE. "Extraordinary faculty . . . to explain ideas and theories of theoretical physics in the language of daily life," ISIS. First part of set covers philosophy of science, drawing upon the practice of Newton, Maxwell, Poincaré, Einstein, others, discussing modes of thought, experiment, interpretations of causality, etc. In the second part, 100 pages explain grammar and vocabulary of mathematics, with discussions of functions, groups, series, Fourier series, etc. The remainder is devoted to concrete, detailed coverage of both classical and quantum physics, explaining such topics as analytic mechanics, Hamilton's principle, wave theory of light, electromagnetic waves, groups of transformations, thermodynamics, phase rule, Brownian movement, kinetics, special relativity, Planck's original quantum theory, Bohr's atom, Zeeman effect, Broglie's wave mechanics, Heisenberg's uncertainty, Eigen-values, matrices, scores of other important topics. Discoveries and theories are covered for such men as Alembert, Born, Cantor, Debye, Euler, Foucault, Galois, Gauss, Hadamard, Kelvin, Kepler, Laplace, Maxwell, Pauli, Rayleigh, Volterra, Weyl, Young, more than 180 others. Indexed. 97 illustrations. ix + 982pp. 5⅜ x 8. T3 Volume 1, Paperbound **$2.25**
T4 Volume 2, Paperbound **$2.25**

SPINNING TOPS AND GYROSCOPIC MOTION, John Perry. Well-known classic of science still unsurpassed for lucid, accurate, delightful exposition. How quasi-rigidity is induced in flexible and fluid bodies by rapid motions; why gyrostat falls, top rises; nature and effect on climatic conditions of earth's precessional movement; effect of internal fluidity on rotating bodies, etc. Appendixes describe practical uses to which gyroscopes have been put in ships, compasses, monorail transportation. 62 figures. 128pp. 5⅜ x 8. T416 Paperbound **$1.25**

THE UNIVERSE OF LIGHT, Sir William Bragg. No scientific training needed to read Nobel Prize winner's expansion of his Royal Institute Christmas Lectures. Insight into nature of light, methods and philosophy of science. Explains lenses, reflection, color, resonance, polarization, x-rays, the spectrum, Newton's work with prisms, Huygens' with polarization, Crookes' with cathode ray, etc. Leads into clear statement of 2 major historical theories of light, corpuscle and wave. Dozens of experiments you can do. 199 illus., including 2 full-page color plates. 293pp. 5⅜ x 8. S538 Paperbound **$1.85**

THE STORY OF X-RAYS FROM RÖNTGEN TO ISOTOPES, A. R. Bleich. Non-technical history of x-rays, their scientific explanation, their applications in medicine, industry, research, and art, and their effect on the individual and his descendants. Includes amusing early reactions to Röntgen's discovery, cancer therapy, detections of art and stamp forgeries, potential risks to patient and operator, etc. Illustrations show x-rays of flower structure, the gall bladder, gears with hidden defects, etc. Original Dover publication. Glossary. Bibliography. Index. 55 photos and figures. xiv + 186pp. 5⅜ x 8. T662 Paperbound **$1.50**

ELECTRONS, ATOMS, METALS AND ALLOYS, Wm. Hume-Rothery. An introductory-level explanation of the application of the electronic theory to the structure and properties of metals and alloys, taking into account the new theoretical work done by mathematical physicists. Material presented in dialogue-form between an "Old Metallurgist" and a "Young Scientist." Their discussion falls into 4 main parts: the nature of an atom, the nature of a metal, the nature of an alloy, and the structure of the nucleus. They cover such topics as the hydrogen atom, electron waves, wave mechanics, Brillouin zones, co-valent bonds, radioactivity and natural disintegration, fundamental particles, structure and fission of the nucleus,etc. Revised, enlarged edition. 177 illustrations. Subject and name indexes. 407pp. 5⅜ x 8½. S1046 Paperbound **$2.25**

BOOKS EXPLAINING SCIENCE AND MATHEMATICS

Engineering, technology, applied science etc.

TEACH YOURSELF ELECTRICITY, C. W. Wilman. Electrical resistance, inductance, capacitance, magnets, chemical effects of current, alternating currents, generators and motors, transformers, rectifiers, much more. 230 questions, answers, worked examples. List of units. 115 illus. 194pp. 6⅞ x 4¼. Clothbound **$2.00**

ELEMENTARY METALLURGY AND METALLOGRAPHY, A. M. Shrager. Basic theory and descriptions of most of the fundamental manufacturing processes involved in metallurgy. Partial contents: the structure of metals; slip, plastic deformation, and recrystalization; iron ore and production of pig iron; chemistry involved in the metallurgy of iron and steel; basic processes such as the Bessemer treatment, open-hearth process, the electric arc furnace —with advantages and disadvantages of each; annealing, hardening, and tempering steel; copper, aluminum, magnesium, and their alloys. For freshman engineers, advanced students in technical high schools, etc. Index. Bibliography. 177 diagrams. 17 tables. 284 questions and problems. 27-page glossary. ix + 389pp. 5⅜ x 8. S138 Paperbound **$2.25**

BASIC ELECTRICITY, Prepared by the Bureau of Naval Personnel. Originally a training course text for U.S. Navy personnel, this book provides thorough coverage of the basic theory of electricity and its applications. Best book of its kind for either broad or more limited studies of electrical fundamentals . . . for classroom use or home study. Part 1 provides a more limited coverage of theory: fundamental concepts, batteries, the simple circuit, D.C. series and parallel circuits, conductors and wiring techniques, A.C. electricity, inductance and capacitance, etc. Part 2 applies theory to the structure of electrical machines—generators, motors, transformers, magnetic amplifiers. Also deals with more complicated instruments, synchros, servo-mechanisms. The concluding chapters cover electrical drawings and blueprints, wiring diagrams, technical manuals, and safety education. The book contains numerous questions for the student, with answers. Index and six appendices. 345 illustrations. x + 448pp. 6½ x 9¼. S973 Paperbound **$3.00**

BASIC ELECTRONICS, prepared by the U.S. Navy Training Publications Center. A thorough and comprehensive manual on the fundamentals of electronics. Written clearly, it is equally useful for self-study or course work for those with a knowledge of the principles of basic electricity. Partial contents: Operating Principles of the Electron Tube; Introduction to Transistors; Power Supplies for Electronic Equipment; Tuned Circuits; Electron-Tube Amplifiers; Audio Power Amplifiers; Oscillators; Transmitters; Transmission Lines; Antennas and Propagation; Introduction to Computers; and related topics. Appendix. Index. Hundreds of illustrations and diagrams. vi + 471pp. 6½ x 9¼. S1076 Paperbound **$2.75**

BASIC THEORY AND APPLICATION OF TRANSISTORS, Prepared by the U.S. Department of the Army. An introductory manual prepared for an army training program. One of the finest available surveys of theory and application of transistor design and operation. Minimal knowledge of physics and theory of electron tubes required. Suitable for textbook use, course supplement, or home study. Chapters: Introduction; fundamental theory of transistors; transistor amplifier fundamentals; parameters, equivalent circuits, and characteristic curves; bias stabilization; transistor analysis and comparison using characteristic curves and charts; audio amplifiers; tuned amplifiers; wide-band amplifiers; oscillators; pulse and switching circuits; modulation, mixing, and demodulation; and additional semiconductor devices. Unabridged, corrected edition. 240 schematic drawings, photographs, wiring diagrams, etc. 2 Appendices. Glossary. Index. 263pp. 6½ x 9¼. S380 Paperbound **$1.25**

TEACH YOURSELF HEAT ENGINES, E. De Ville. Measurement of heat, development of steam and internal combustion engines, efficiency of an engine, compression-ignition engines, production of steam, the ideal engine, much more. 318 exercises, answers, worked examples. Tables. 76 illus. 220pp. 6⅞ x 4¼. Clothbound **$2.25**

BOOKS EXPLAINING SCIENCE AND MATHEMATICS

Miscellaneous

ON THE SENSATIONS OF TONE, Hermann Helmholtz. This is an unmatched coordination of such fields as acoustical physics, physiology, experiment, history of music. It covers the entire gamut of musical tone. Partial contents: relation of musical science to acoustics, physical vs. physiological acoustics, composition of vibration, resonance, analysis of tones by sympathetic resonance, beats, chords, tonality, consonant chords, discords, progression of parts, etc. 33 appendixes discuss various aspects of sound, physics, acoustics, music, etc. Translated by A. J. Ellis. New introduction by Prof. Henry Margenau of Yale. 68 figures. 43 musical passages analyzed. Over 100 tables. Index. xix + 576pp. 6⅛ x 9¼. S114 Paperbound **$3.50**

Catalogue of Dover Books

MATHEMATICS, ELEMENTARY TO INTERMEDIATE

HOW TO CALCULATE QUICKLY, Henry Sticker. This handy volume offers a tried and true method for helping you in the basic mathematics of daily life—addition, subtraction, multiplication, division, fractions, etc. It is designed to awaken your "number sense" or the ability to see relationships between numbers as whole quantities. It is not a collection of tricks working only on special numbers, but a serious course of over 9,000 problems and their solutions, teaching special techniques not taught in schools: left-to-right multiplication, new fast ways of division, etc. 5 or 10 minutes daily use will double or triple your calculation speed. Excellent for the scientific worker who is at home in higher math, but is not satisfied with his speed and accuracy in lower mathematics. 256pp. 5 x 7¼.   T295 Paperbound **$1.00**

TEACH YOURSELF books. For adult self-study, for refresher and supplementary study.

The most effective series of home study mathematics books on the market! With absolutely no outside help, they will teach you as much as any similar college or high-school course, or will helpfully supplement any such course. Each step leads directly to the next, each question is anticipated. Numerous lucid examples and carefully-wrought practice problems illustrate meanings. Not skimpy outlines, not surveys, not usual classroom texts, these 204- to 380-page books are packed with the finest instruction you'll find anywhere for adult self-study.

TEACH YOURSELF ALGEBRA, P. Abbott. Formulas, coordinates, factors, graphs of quadratic functions, quadratic equations, logarithms, ratio, irrational numbers, arithmetical, geometrical series, much more. 1241 problems, solutions. Tables. 52 illus. 307pp. 6⅞ x 4¼.
Clothbound **$2.00**

TEACH YOURSELF GEOMETRY, P. Abbott. Solids, lines, points, surfaces, angle measurement, triangles, theorem of Pythagoras, polygons, loci, the circle, tangents, symmetry, solid geometry, prisms, pyramids, solids of revolution, etc. 343 problems, solutions. 268 illus. 334pp. 6⅞ x 4¼.
Clothbound **$2.00**

TEACH YOURSELF TRIGONOMETRY, P. Abbott. Geometrical foundations, indices, logarithms, trigonometrical ratios, relations between sides, angles of triangle, circular measure, trig. ratios of angles of any magnitude, much more. Requires elementary algebra, geometry. 465 problems, solutions. Tables. 102 illus. 204pp. 6⅞ x 4¼.   Clothbound **$2.00**

TEACH YOURSELF THE CALCULUS, P. Abbott. Variations in functions, differentiation, solids of revolution, series, elementary differential equations, areas by integral calculus, much more. Requires algebra, trigonometry. 970 problems, solutions. Tables. 89 illus. 380pp. 6⅞ x 4¼.
Clothbound **$2.00**

TEACH YOURSELF THE SLIDE RULE, B. Snodgrass. Fractions, decimals, A-D scales, log-log scales, trigonometrical scales, indices, logarithms. Commercial, precision, electrical, dualistic, Brighton rules. 80 problems, solutions. 10 illus. 207pp. 6⅞ x 4¼.   Clothbound **$2.00**

ARITHMETICAL EXCURSIONS: AN ENRICHMENT OF ELEMENTARY MATHEMATICS, H. Bowers and J. Bowers. For students who want unusual methods of arithmetic never taught in school; for adults who want to increase their number sense. Little known facts about the most simple numbers, arithmetical entertainments and puzzles, figurate numbers, number chains, mysteries and folklore of numbers, the "Hin-dog-abic" number system, etc. First publication. Index. 529 numbered problems and diversions, all with answers. Bibliography. 50 figures. xiv + 320pp. 5⅜ x 8.   T770 Paperbound **$1.65**

HOW DO YOU USE A SLIDE RULE? by A. A. Merrill. Not a manual for mathematicians and engineers, but a lucid step-by-step explanation that presents the fundamental rules clearly enough to be understood by anyone who could benefit by the use of a slide rule in his work or business. This work concentrates on the 2 most important operations: multiplication and division. 10 easy lessons, each with a clear drawing, will save you countless hours in your banking, business, statistical, and other work. First publication. Index. 2 Appendixes. 10 illustrations. 78 problems, all with answers. vi + 36pp. 6⅛ x 9¼.   T62 Paperbound **60¢**

THE THEORY AND OPERATION OF THE SLIDE RULE, J. P. Ellis. Not a skimpy "instruction manual", but an exhaustive treatment that will save you hours throughout your career. Supplies full understanding of every scale on the Log Log Duplex Decitrig type of slide rule. Shows the most time-saving methods, and provides practice useful in the widest variety of actual engineering situations. Each operation introduced in terms of underlying logarithmic theory. Summary of prerequisite math. First publication. Index. 198 figures. Over 450 problems with answers. Bibliography. 12 Appendices. ix + 289pp. 5⅜ x 8.
S727 Paperbound **$1.50**

Catalogue of Dover Books

COLLEGE ALGEBRA, H. B. Fine. Standard college text that gives a systematic and deductive structure to algebra; comprehensive, connected, with emphasis on theory. Discusses the commutative, associative, and distributive laws of number in unusual detail, and goes on with undetermined coefficients, quadratic equations, progressions, logarithms, permutations, probability, power series, and much more. Still most valuable elementary-intermediate text on the science and structure of algebra. Index. 1560 problems, all with answers. x + 631pp. 5⅜ x 8.					T211 Paperbound **$2.75**

COORDINATE GEOMETRY, L. P. Eisenhart. Thorough, unified introduction. Unusual for advancing in dimension within each topic (treats together circle, sphere; polar coordinates, 3-dimensional coordinate systems; conic sections, quadric surfaces), affording exceptional insight into subject. Extensive use made of determinants, though no previous knowledge of them is assumed. Algebraic equations of 1st degree, 2 and 3 unknowns, carried further than usual in algebra courses. Over 500 exercises. Introduction. Appendix. Index. Bibliography. 43 illustrations. 310pp. 5⅜ x 8.				S600 Paperbound **$1.65**

A TREATISE ON PLANE AND ADVANCED TRIGONOMETRY, E. W. Hobson. Extraordinarily wide coverage, going beyond usual college level trig, one of the few works covering advanced trig in full detail. By a great expositor with unerring anticipation and lucid clarification of potentially difficult points. Includes circular functions; expansion of functions of multiple angle; trig tables; relations between sides and angles of triangle; complex numbers; etc. Many problems solved completely. "The best work on the subject." Nature. Formerly entitled "A Treatise on Plane Trigonometry." 689 examples. 6 figures. xvi + 383pp. 5⅜ x 8.
					S353 Paperbound **$2.25**

FAMOUS PROBLEMS OF ELEMENTARY GEOMETRY, Felix Klein. Expanded version of the 1894 Easter lectures at Göttingen. 3 problems of classical geometry, in an excellent mathematical treatment by a famous mathematician: squaring the circle, trisecting angle, doubling cube. Considered with full modern implications: transcendental numbers, pi, etc. Notes by R. Archibald. 16 figures. xi + 92pp. 5⅜ x 8.				T298 Paperbound **$1.00**

MONOGRAPHS ON TOPICS OF MODERN MATHEMATICS, edited by J. W. A. Young. Advanced mathematics for persons who haven't gone beyond or have forgotten high school algebra. 9 monographs on foundation of geometry, modern pure geometry, non-Euclidean geometry, fundamental propositions of algebra, algebraic equations, functions, calculus, theory of numbers, etc. Each monograph gives proofs of important results, and descriptions of leading methods, to provide wide coverage. New introduction by Prof. M. Kline, N. Y. University. 100 diagrams. xvi + 416pp. 6⅛ x 9¼.				S289 Paperbound **$2.00**

HIGHER MATHEMATICS FOR STUDENTS OF CHEMISTRY AND PHYSICS, J. W. Mellor. Not abstract, but practical, building its problems out of familiar laboratory material, this covers differential calculus, coordinate, analytical geometry, functions, integral calculus, infinite series, numerical equations, differential equations, Fourier's theorem, probability, theory of errors, calculus of variations, determinants. "If the reader is not familiar with this book, it will repay him to examine it," CHEM. & ENGINEERING NEWS. 800 problems. 189 figures. Bibliography. xxi + 641pp. 5⅜ x 8.				S193 Paperbound **$2.50**

TRIGONOMETRY REFRESHER FOR TECHNICAL MEN, A. Albert Klaf. 913 detailed questions and answers cover the most important aspects of plane and spherical trigonometry. They will help you to brush up or to clear up difficulties in special areas. The first portion of this book covers plane trigonometry, including angles, quadrants, trigonometrical functions, graphical representation, interpolation, equations, logarithms, solution of triangle, use of the slide rule and similar topics. 188 pages then discuss application of plane trigonometry to special problems in navigation, surveying, elasticity, architecture, and various fields of engineering. Small angles, periodic functions, vectors, polar coordinates, de Moivre's theorem are fully examined. The third section of the book then discusses spherical trigonometry and the solution of spherical triangles, with their applications to terrestrial and astronomical problems. Methods of saving time with numerical calculations, simplification of principal functions of angle, much practical information make this a most useful book. 913 questions answered. 1738 problems, answers to odd numbers. 494 figures. 24 pages of useful formulae, functions. Index. x + 629pp. 5⅜ x 8.				T371 Paperbound **$2.00**

TEXTBOOK OF ALGEBRA, G. Chrystal. One of the great mathematical textbooks, still about the best source for complete treatments of the topics of elementary algebra; a chief reference work for teachers and students of algebra in advanced high school and university courses, or for the mathematician working on problems of elementary algebra or looking for a background to more advanced topics. Ranges from basic laws and processes to extensive examination of such topics as limits, infinite series, general properties of integral numbers, and probability theory. Emphasis is on algebraic form, the foundation of analytical geometry and the key to modern developments in algebra. Prior course in algebra is desirable, but not absolutely necessary. Includes theory of quotients, distribution of products, arithmetical theory of surds, theory of interest, permutations and combinations, general expansion theorems, recurring fractions, and much, much more. Two volume set. Index in each volume. Over 1500 exercises, approximately half with answers. Total of xlviii + 1187pp. 5⅜ x 8.
					S750 Vol I Paperbound **$2.35**
					S751 Vol II Paperbound **$2.35**
					The set **$4.70**

MATHEMATICS, HISTORIES AND CLASSICS

HISTORY OF MATHEMATICS, D. E. Smith. Most comprehensive non-technical history of math in English. Discusses lives and works of over a thousand major and minor figures, with footnotes supplying technical information outside the book's scheme, and indicating disputed matters. Vol I: A chronological examination, from primitive concepts through Egypt, Babylonia, Greece, the Orient, Rome, the Middle Ages, the Renaissance, and up to 1900. Vol 2: The development of ideas in specific fields and problems, up through elementary calculus. Two volumes, total of 510 illustrations, 1355pp. 5⅜ x 8. Set boxed in attractive container.   T429, 430 Paperbound, the set **$5.00**

A SHORT ACCOUNT OF THE HISTORY OF MATHEMATICS, W. W. R. Ball. Most readable non-technical history of mathematics treats lives, discoveries of every important figure from Egyptian, Phoenician mathematicians to late 19th century. Discusses schools of Ionia, Pythagoras, Athens, Cyzicus, Alexandria, Byzantium, systems of numeration; primitive arithmetic; Middle Ages, Renaissance, including Arabs, Bacon, Regiomontanus, Tartaglia, Cardan, Stevinus, Galileo, Kepler; modern mathematics of Descartes, Pascal, Wallis, Huygens, Newton, Leibnitz, d'Alembert, Euler, Lambert, Laplace, Legendre, Gauss, Hermite, Weierstrass, scores more. Index. 25 figures. 546pp. 5⅜ x 8.   S630 Paperbound **$2.25**

A HISTORY OF GEOMETRICAL METHODS, J. L. Coolidge. Full, authoritative history of the techniques which men have employed in dealing with geometric questions . . . from ancient times to the modern development of projective geometry. Critical analyses of the original works. Contents: Synthetic Geometry—the early beginnings, Greek mathematics, non-Euclidean geometries, projective and descriptive geometry; Algebraic Geometry—extension of the system of linear coordinates, other systems of point coordinates, enumerative and birational geometry, etc.; and Differential Geometry—intrinsic geometry and moving axes, Gauss and the classical theory of surfaces, and projective and absolute differential geometry. The work of scores of geometers analyzed: Pythagoras, Archimedes, Newton, Descartes, Leibniz, Lobachevski, Riemann, Hilbert, Bernoulli, Schubert, Grassman, Klein, Cauchy, and many, many others. Extensive (24-page) bibliography. Index. 13 figures. xviii + 451pp. 5⅜ x 8½.   S1006 Paperbound **$2.25**

THE MATHEMATICS OF GREAT AMATEURS, Julian Lowell Coolidge. Enlightening, often surprising, accounts of what can result from a non-professional preoccupation with mathematics. Chapters on Plato, Omar Khayyam and his work with cubic equations, Piero della Francesca, Albrecht Dürer, as the true discoverer of descriptive geometry, Leonardo da Vinci and his varied mathematical interests, John Napier, Baron of Merchiston, inventor of logarithms, Pascal, Diderot, l'Hospital, and seven others known primarily for contributions in other fields. Bibliography. 56 figures. viii + 211pp. 5⅜ x 8½.   S1009 Paperbound **$1.50**

ART AND GEOMETRY, Wm. M. Ivins, Jr. A controversial study which propounds the view that the ideas of Greek philosophy and culture served not to stimulate, but to stifle the development of Western thought. Through an examination of Greek art and geometrical inquiries and Renaissance experiments, this book offers a concise history of the evolution of mathematical perspective and projective geometry. Discusses the work of Alberti, Dürer, Pelerin, Nicholas of Cusa, Kepler, Desargues, etc. in a wholly readable text of interest to the art historian, philosopher, mathematician, historian of science, and others. x + 113pp. 5⅜ x 8⅜.   T941 Paperbound **$1.00**

A SOURCE BOOK IN MATHEMATICS, D. E. Smith. Great discoveries in math, from Renaissance to end of 19th century, in English translation. Read announcements by Dedekind, Gauss, Delamain, Pascal, Fermat, Newton, Abel, Lobachevsky, Bolyai, Riemann, De Moivre, Legendre, Laplace, others of discoveries about imaginary numbers, number congruence, slide rule, equations, symbolism, cubic algebraic equations, non-Euclidean forms of geometry, calculus, function theory, quaternions, etc. Succinct selections from 125 different treatises, articles, most unavailable elsewhere in English. Each article preceded by biographical, historical introduction. Vol. I: Fields of Number, Algebra. Index. 32 illus. 338pp. 5⅜ x 8. Vol. II: Fields of Geometry, Probability, Calculus, Functions, Quaternions. 83 illus. 432pp. 5⅜ x 8.
Vol. 1: S552 Paperbound **$2.00**
Vol. 2: S553 Paperbound **$2.00**
2 vol. set, **$4.00**

A COLLECTION OF MODERN MATHEMATICAL CLASSICS, edited by R. Bellman. 13 classic papers, complete in their original languages, by Hermite, Hardy and Littlewood, Tchebychef, Fejér, Fredholm, Fuchs, Hurwitz, Weyl, van der Pol, Birkhoff, Kellogg, von Neumann, and Hilbert. Each of these papers, collected here for the first time, triggered a burst of mathematical activity, providing useful new generalizations or stimulating fresh investigations. Topics discussed include classical analysis, periodic and almost periodic functions, analysis and number theory, integral equations, theory of approximation, non-linear differential equations, and functional analysis. Brief introductions and bibliographies to each paper. xii + 292pp. 6 x 9.
S730 Paperbound **$2.00**

THE WORKS OF ARCHIMEDES, edited by T. L. Heath. All the known works of the great Greek mathematician are contained in this one volume, including the recently discovered Method of Archimedes. Contains: On Sphere & Cylinder, Measurement of a Circle, Spirals, Conoids, Spheroids, etc. This is the definitive edition of the greatest mathematical intellect of the ancient world. 186-page study by Heath discusses Archimedes and the history of Greek mathematics. Bibliography. 563pp. 5⅜ x 8.   S9 Paperbound **$2.45**

PHYSICS

General physics

FOUNDATIONS OF PHYSICS, R. B. Lindsay & H. Margenau. Excellent bridge between semi-popular works & technical treatises. A discussion of methods of physical description, construction of theory; valuable for physicist who is interested in ideas that give meaning to data, tools of modern physics. Contents include symbolism, mathematical equations; space & time foundations of mechanics; probability; physics & continua; electron theory; special & general relativity; quantum mechanics; causality. "Thorough and yet not overdetailed. Unreservedly recommended," NATURE (London). Unabridged, corrected edition. List of recommended readings. 35 illustrations. xi + 537pp. 5⅜ x 8.
S377 Paperbound **$3.00**

FUNDAMENTAL FORMULAS OF PHYSICS, ed. by D. H. Menzel. Highly useful, fully inexpensive reference and study text, ranging from simple to highly sophisticated operations. Mathematics integrated into text—each chapter stands as short textbook of field represented. Vol. 1: Statistics, Physical Constants, Special Theory of Relativity, Hydrodynamics, Aerodynamics, Boundary Value Problems in Math. Physics; Viscosity, Electromagnetic Theory, etc. Vol. 2: Sound, Acoustics, Geometrical Optics, Electron Optics, High-Energy Phenomena, Magnetism, Biophysics, much more. Index. Total of 800pp. 5⅜ x 8.
Vol. 1 S595 Paperbound **$2.25**
Vol. 2 S596 Paperbound **$2.25**

MATHEMATICAL PHYSICS, D. H. Menzel. Thorough one-volume treatment of the mathematical techniques vital for classic mechanics, electromagnetic theory, quantum theory, and relativity. Written by the Harvard Professor of Astrophysics for junior, senior, and graduate courses, it gives clear explanations of all those aspects of function theory, vectors, matrices, dyadics, tensors, partial differential equations, etc., necessary for the understanding of the various physical theories. Electron theory, relativity, and other topics seldom presented appear here in considerable detail. Scores of definitions, conversion factors, dimensional constants, etc. "More detailed than normal for an advanced text . . . excellent set of sections on Dyadics, Matrices, and Tensors," JOURNAL OF THE FRANKLIN INSTITUTE. Index. 193 problems, with answers. x + 412pp. 5⅜ x 8.
S56 Paperbound **$2.00**

THE SCIENTIFIC PAPERS OF J. WILLARD GIBBS. All the published papers of America's outstanding theoretical scientist (except for "Statistical Mechanics" and "Vector Analysis"). Vol I (thermodynamics) contains one of the most brilliant of all 19th-century scientific papers—the 300-page "On the Equilibrium of Heterogeneous Substances," which founded the science of physical chemistry, and clearly stated a number of highly important natural laws for the first time; 8 other papers complete the first volume. Vol II includes 2 papers on dynamics, 8 on vector analysis and multiple algebra, 5 on the electromagnetic theory of light, and 6 miscellaneous papers. Biographical sketch by H. A. Bumstead. Total of xxxvi + 718pp. 5⅝ x 8⅜.
S721 Vol I Paperbound **$2.50**
S722 Vol II Paperbound **$2.00**
The set **$4.50**

BASIC THEORIES OF PHYSICS, Peter Gabriel Bergmann. Two-volume set which presents a critical examination of important topics in the major subdivisions of classical and modern physics. The first volume is concerned with classical mechanics and electrodynamics: mechanics of mass points, analytical mechanics, matter in bulk, electrostatics and magnetostatics, electromagnetic interaction, the field waves, special relativity, and waves. The second volume (Heat and Quanta) contains discussions of the kinetic hypothesis, physics and statistics, stationary ensembles, laws of thermodynamics, early quantum theories, atomic spectra, probability waves, quantization in wave mechanics, approximation methods, and abstract quantum theory. A valuable supplement to any thorough course or text.
Heat and Quanta: Index. 8 figures. x + 300pp. 5⅜ x 8½. S968 Paperbound **$2.00**
Mechanics and Electrodynamics: Index. 14 figures. vii + 280pp. 5⅜ x 8½.
S969 Paperbound **$1.85**

THEORETICAL PHYSICS, A. S. Kompaneyets. One of the very few thorough studies of the subject in this price range. Provides advanced students with a comprehensive theoretical background. Especially strong on recent experimentation and developments in quantum theory. Contents: Mechanics (Generalized Coordinates, Lagrange's Equation, Collision of Particles, etc.), Electrodynamics (Vector Analysis, Maxwell's equations, Transmission of Signals, Theory of Relativity, etc.), Quantum Mechanics (the Inadequacy of Classical Mechanics, the Wave Equation, Motion in a Central Field, Quantum Theory of Radiation, Quantum Theories of Dispersion and Scattering, etc.), and Statistical Physics (Equilibrium Distribution of Molecules in an Ideal Gas, Boltzmann statistics, Bose and Fermi Distribution, Thermodynamic Quantities, etc.). Revised to 1961. Translated by George Yankovsky, authorized by Kompaneyets. 137 exercises. 56 figures. 529pp. 5⅜ x 8½. S972 Paperbound **$2.50**

ANALYTICAL AND CANONICAL FORMALISM IN PHYSICS, André Mercier. A survey, in one volume, of the variational principles (the key principles—in mathematical form—from which the basic laws of any one branch of physics can be derived) of the several branches of physical theory, together with an examination of the relationships among them. Contents: the Lagrangian Formalism, Lagrangian Densities, Canonical Formalism, Canonical Form of Electrodynamics, Hamiltonian Densities, Transformations, and Canonical Form with Vanishing Jacobian Determinant. Numerous examples and exercises. For advanced students, teachers, etc. 6 figures. Index. viii + 222pp. 5⅜ x 8½. S1077 Paperbound **$1.75**

CHEMISTRY AND PHYSICAL CHEMISTRY

ORGANIC CHEMISTRY, F. C. Whitmore. The entire subject of organic chemistry for the practicing chemist and the advanced student. Storehouse of facts, theories, processes found elsewhere only in specialized journals. Covers aliphatic compounds (500 pages on the properties and synthetic preparation of hydrocarbons, halides, proteins, ketones, etc.), alicyclic compounds, aromatic compounds, heterocyclic compounds, organophosphorus and organometallic compounds. Methods of synthetic preparation analyzed critically throughout. Includes much of biochemical interest. "The scope of this volume is astonishing," INDUSTRIAL AND ENGINEERING CHEMISTRY. 12,000-reference index. 2387-item bibliography. Total of x + 1005pp. 5⅜ x 8.
Two volume set.
S700 Vol I Paperbound **$2.25**
S701 Vol II Paperbound **$2.25**
The set **$4.50**

THE MODERN THEORY OF MOLECULAR STRUCTURE, Bernard Pullman. A reasonably popular account of recent developments in atomic and molecular theory. Contents: The Wave Function and Wave Equations (history and bases of present theories of molecular structure); The Electronic Structure of Atoms (Description and classification of atomic wave functions, etc.); Diatomic Molecules; Non-Conjugated Polyatomic Molecules; Conjugated Polyatomic Molecules; The Structure of Complexes. Minimum of mathematical background needed. New translation by David Antin of "La Structure Moleculaire." Index. Bibliography. vii + 87pp. 5⅜ x 8½.
S987 Paperbound **$1.00**

CATALYSIS AND CATALYSTS, Marcel Prettre, Director, Research Institute on Catalysis. This brief book, translated into English for the first time, is the finest summary of the principal modern concepts, methods, and results of catalysis. Ideal introduction for beginning chemistry and physics students. Chapters: Basic Definitions of Catalysis (true catalysis and generalization of the concept of catalysis); The Scientific Bases of Catalysis (Catalysis and chemical thermodynamics, catalysis and chemical kinetics); Homogeneous Catalysis (acid-base catalysis, etc.); Chain Reactions; Contact Masses; Heterogeneous Catalysis (Mechanisms of contact catalyses, etc.); and Industrial Applications (acids and fertilizers, petroleum and petroleum chemistry, rubber, plastics, synthetic resins, and fibers). Translated by David Antin. Index. vi + 88pp. 5⅜ x 8½.
S998 Paperbound **$1.00**

POLAR MOLECULES, Pieter Debye. This work by Nobel laureate Debye offers a complete guide to fundamental electrostatic field relations, polarizability, molecular structure. Partial contents: electric intensity, displacement and force, polarization by orientation, molar polarization and molar refraction, halogen-hydrides, polar liquids, ionic saturation, dielectric constant, etc. Special chapter considers quantum theory. Indexed. 172pp. 5⅜ x 8.
S64 Paperbound **$1.65**

THE ELECTRONIC THEORY OF ACIDS AND BASES, W. F. Luder and Saverio Zuffanti. The first full systematic presentation of the electronic theory of acids and bases—treating the theory and its ramifications in an uncomplicated manner. Chapters: Historical Background; Atomic Orbitals and Valence; The Electronic Theory of Acids and Bases; Electrophilic and Electrodotic Reagents; Acidic and Basic Radicals; Neutralization; Titrations with Indicators; Displacement; Catalysis; Acid Catalysis; Base Catalysis; Alkoxides and Catalysts; Conclusion. Required reading for all chemists. Second revised (1961) eidtion, with additional examples and references. 3 figures. 9 tables. Index. Bibliography xii + 165pp. 5⅜ x 8.
S201 Paperbound **$1.50**

KINETIC THEORY OF LIQUIDS, J. Frenkel. Regarding the kinetic theory of liquids as a generalization and extension of the theory of solid bodies, this volume covers all types of arrangements of solids, thermal displacements of atoms, interstitial atoms and ions, orientational and rotational motion of molecules, and transition between states of matter. Mathematical theory is developed close to the physical subject matter. 216 bibliographical footnotes. 55 figures. xi + 485pp. 5⅜ x 8.
S95 Paperbound **$2.55**

THE PRINCIPLES OF ELECTROCHEMISTRY, D. A. MacInnes. Basic equations for almost every subfield of electrochemistry from first principles, referring at all times to the soundest and most recent theories and results; unusually useful as text or as reference. Covers coulometers and Faraday's Law, electrolytic conductance, the Debye-Hueckel method for the theoretical calculation of activity coefficients, concentration cells, standard electrode potentials, thermodynamic ionization constants, pH, potentiometric titrations, irreversible phenomena, Planck's equation, and much more. "Excellent treatise," AMERICAN CHEMICAL SOCIETY JOURNAL. "Highly recommended," CHEMICAL AND METALLURGICAL ENGINEERING. 2 Indices. Appendix. 585-item bibliography. 137 figures. 94 tables. ii + 478pp. 5⅝ x 8⅜.
S52 Paperbound **$2.45**

THE PHASE RULE AND ITS APPLICATION, Alexander Findlay. Covering chemical phenomena of 1, 2, 3, 4, and multiple component systems, this "standard work on the subject" (NATURE, London), has been completely revised and brought up to date by A. N. Campbell and N. O. Smith. Brand new material has been added on such matters as binary, tertiary liquid equilibria, solid solutions in ternary systems, quinary systems of salts and water. Completely revised to triangular coordinates in ternary systems, clarified graphic representation, solid models, etc. 9th revised edition. Author, subject indexes. 236 figures. 505 footnotes, mostly bibliographic. xii + 494pp. 5⅜ x 8.
S91 Paperbound **$2.50**

THE SOLUBILITY OF NONELECTROLYTES, Joel H. Hildebrand and Robert L. Scott. The standard work on the subject; still indispensable as a reference source and for classroom work. Partial contents: The Ideal Solution (including Raoult's Law and Henry's Law, etc.); Nonideal Solutions; Intermolecular Forces; The Liquid State; Entropy of Athermal Mixing; Heat of Mixing; Polarity; Hydrogen Bonding; Specific Interactions; "Solvation" and "Association"; Systems of Three or More Components; Vapor Pressure of Binary Liquid Solutions; Mixtures of Gases; Solubility of Gases in Liquids; of Liquids in Liquids; of Solids in Liquids; Evaluation of Solubility Parameters; and other topics. Corrected republication of third (revised) edition. Appendices. Indexes. 138 figures. 111 tables. 1 photograph. iv + 488pp. 5⅜ x 8½.
S1125 Paperbound **$2.50**

TERNARY SYSTEMS: INTRODUCTION TO THE THEORY OF THREE COMPONENT SYSTEMS, G. Masing. Furnishes detailed discussion of representative types of 3-components systems, both in solid models (particularly metallic alloys) and isothermal models. Discusses mechanical mixture without compounds and without solid solutions; unbroken solid solution series; solid solutions with solubility breaks in two binary systems; iron-silicon-aluminum alloys; allotropic forms of iron in ternary system; other topics. Bibliography. Index. 166 illustrations. 178pp. 5⅝ x 8⅜.
S631 Paperbound **$1.50**

THE KINETIC THEORY OF GASES, Leonard B. Loeb, University of California. Comprehensive text and reference book which presents full coverage of basic theory and the important experiments and developments in the field for the student and investigator. Partial contents: The Mechanical Picture of a Perfect Gas, The Mean Free Path—Clausius' Deductions, Distribution of Molecular Velocities, discussions of theory of the problem of specific heats, the contributions of kinetic theory to our knowledge of electrical and magnetic properties of molecules and its application to the conduction of electricity in gases. New 14-page preface to Dover edition by the author. Name, subject indexes. Six appendices. 570-item bibliography. xxxvi + 687pp. 5⅜ x 8½.
S942 Paperbound **$3.50**

IONS IN SOLUTION, Ronald W. Gurney. A thorough and readable introduction covering all the fundamental principles and experiments in the field, by an internationally-known authority. Contains discussions of solvation energy, atomic and molecular ions, lattice energy, transferral of ions, interionic forces, cells and half-cells, transference of electrons, exchange forces, hydrogen ions, the electro-chemical series, and many other related topics. Indispensable to advanced undergraduates and graduate students in electrochemistry. Index. 45 illustrations. 15 tables. vii + 206pp. 5⅜ x 8½.
S124 Paperbound **$1.‍15**

IONIC PROCESSES IN SOLUTION, Ronald W. Gurney. Lucid, comprehensive examination which brings together the approaches of electrochemistry, thermodynamics, statistical mechanics, electroacoustics, molecular physics, and quantum theory in the interpretation of the behavior of ionic solutions—the most important single work on the subject. More extensive and technical than the author's earlier work (IONS IN SOLUTION), it is a middle-level text for graduate students and researchers in electrochemistry. Covers such matters as Brownian motion in liquids, molecular ions in solution, heat of precipitation, entropy of solution, proton transfers, dissociation constant of nitric acid, viscosity of ionic solutions, etc. 78 illustrations. 47 tables. Name and subject index. ix + 275pp. 5⅜ x 8½.
S134 Paperbound **$1.85**

CRYSTALLOGRAPHIC DATA ON METAL AND ALLOY STRUCTURES, Compiled by A. Taylor and B. J. Kagle, Westinghouse Research Laboratories. Unique collection of the latest crystallographic data on alloys, compounds, and the elements, with lattice spacings expressed uniformly in absolute Angstrom units. Gathers together previously widely-scattered data from the Power Data File of the ATSM, structure reports, and the Landolt-Bornstein Tables, as well as from other original literature. 2300 different compounds listed in the first table, Alloys and Intermetallic Compounds, with much vital information on each. Also listings for nearly 700 Borides, Carbides, Hydrides, Oxides, Nitrides. Also all the necessary data on the crystal structure of 77 elements. vii + 263pp. 5⅜ x 8.
S1013 Paperbound **$2.25**

MATHEMATICAL CRYSTALLOGRAPHY AND THE THEORY OF GROUPS OF MOVEMENTS, Harold Hilton. Classic account of the mathematical theory of crystallography, particularly the geometrical theory of crystal-structure based on the work of Bravais, Jordan, Sohncke, Federow, Schoenflies, and Barlow. Partial contents: The Stereographic Projection, Properties Common to Symmetrical and Asymmetrical Crystals, The Theory of Groups, Coordinates of Equivalent Points, Crystallographic Axes and Axial Ratios, The Forms and Growth of Crystals, Lattices and Translations, The Structure-Theory, Infinite Groups of Movements, Triclinic and Monoclinic Groups, Orthorhombic Groups, etc. Index. 188 figures. xii + 262pp. 5⅜ x 8½.
S1058 Paperbound **$2.00**

CLASSICS IN THE THEORY OF CHEMICAL COMBINATIONS. Edited by O. T. Benfey. Vol. I of the Classics of Science Series, G. Holton, Harvard University, General Editor. This book is a collection of papers representing the major chapters in the development of the valence concept in chemistry. Includes essays by Wöhler and Liebig, Laurent, Williamson, Frankland, Kekulé and Couper, and two by van't Hoff and le Bel, which mark the first extension of the valence concept beyond its purely numerical character. Introduction and epilogue by Prof. Benfey. Index. 9 illustrations. New translation of Kekulé paper by Benfey. xiv + 191pp. 5⅜ x 8½.
S1066 Paperbound **$1.85**

ENGINEERING AND TECHNOLOGY

General and mathematical

ENGINEERING MATHEMATICS, Kenneth S. Miller. A text for graduate students of engineering to strengthen their mathematical background in differential equations, etc. Mathematical steps very explicitly indicated. Contents: Determinants and Matrices, Integrals, Linear Differential Equations, Fourier Series and Integrals, Laplace Transform, Network Theory, Random Function . . . all vital requisites for advanced modern engineering studies. Unabridged republication. Appendices: Borel Sets; Riemann-Stieltjes Integral; Fourier Series and Integrals. Index. References at Chapter Ends. xii + 417pp. 6 x 8½. S1121 Paperbound **$2.00**

MATHEMATICAL ENGINEERING ANALYSIS, Rufus Oldenburger. A book designed to assist the research engineer and scientist in making the transition from physical engineering situations to the corresponding mathematics. Scores of common practical situations found in all major fields of physics are supplied with their correct mathematical formulations—applications to automobile springs and shock absorbers, clocks, throttle torque of diesel engines, resistance networks, capacitors, transmission lines, microphones, neon tubes, gasoline engines, refrigeration cycles, etc. Each section reviews basic principles of underlying various fields: mechanics of rigid bodies, electricity and magnetism, heat, elasticity, fluid mechanics, and aerodynamics. Comprehensive and eminently useful. Index. 169 problems, answers. 200 photos and diagrams. xiv + 426pp. 5⅜ x 8½. S919 Paperbound $2.50

MATHEMATICS OF MODERN ENGINEERING, E. G. Keller and R. E. Doherty. Written for the Advanced Course in Engineering of the General Electric Corporation, deals with the engineering use of determinants, tensors, the Heaviside operational calculus, dyadics, the calculus of variations, etc. Presents underlying principles fully, but purpose is to teach engineers to deal with modern engineering problems, and emphasis is on the perennial engineering attack of set-up and solve. Indexes. Over 185 figures and tables. Hundreds of exercises, problems, and worked-out examples. References. Two volume set. Total of xxxiii + 623pp. 5⅜ x 8.
S734 Vol I Paperbound **$1.85**
S735 Vol II Paperbound **$1.85**
The set **$3.70**

MATHEMATICAL METHODS FOR SCIENTISTS AND ENGINEERS, L. P. Smith. For scientists and engineers, as well as advanced math students. Full investigation of methods and practical description of conditions under which each should be used. Elements of real functions, differential and integral calculus, space geometry, theory of residues, vector and tensor analysis, series of Bessel functions, etc. Each method illustrated by completely-worked-out examples, mostly from scientific literature. 368 graded unsolved problems. 100 diagrams. x + 453pp. 5⅝ x 8⅜. S220 Paperbound **$2.00**

THEORY OF FUNCTIONS AS APPLIED TO ENGINEERING PROBLEMS, edited by R. Rothe, F. Ollendorff, and K. Pohlhausen. A series of lectures given at the Berlin Institute of Technology that shows the specific applications of function theory in electrical and allied fields of engineering. Six lectures provide the elements of function theory in a simple and practical form, covering complex quantities and variables, integration in the complex plane, residue theorems, etc. Then 5 lectures show the exact uses of this powerful mathematical tool, with full discussions of problem methods. Index. Bibliography. 108 figures. x + 189pp. 5⅜ x 8.
S733 Paperbound **$1.35**

Aerodynamics and hydrodynamics

AIRPLANE STRUCTURAL ANALYSIS AND DESIGN, E. E. Sechler and L. G. Dunn. Systematic authoritative book which summarizes a large amount of theoretical and experimental work on structural analysis and design. Strong on classical subsonic material still basic to much aeronautic design . . . remains a highly useful source of information. Covers such areas as layout of the airplane, applied and design loads, stress-strain relationships for stable structures, truss and frame analysis, the problem of instability, the ultimate strength of stiffened flat sheet, analysis of cylindrical structures, wings and control surfaces, fuselage analysis, engine mounts, landing gears, etc. Oɪ ₋.nally published as part of the CALCIT Aeronautical Series. 256 Illustrations. 47 study problems. Indexes. xi + 420pp. 5⅜ x 8½.
S1043 Paperbound **$2.25**

FUNDAMENTALS OF HYDRO- AND AEROMECHANICS, L. Prandtl and O. G. Tietjens. The well-known standard work based upon Prandtl's lectures at Goettingen. Wherever possible hydrodynamics theory is referred to practical considerations in hydraulics, with the view of unifying theory and experience. Presentation is extremely clear and though primarily physical, mathematical proofs are rigorous and use vector analysis to a considerable extent. An Enginering Society Monograph, 1934. 186 figures. Index. xvi + 270pp. 5⅜ x 8.
S374 Paperbound **$1.85**

FLUID MECHANICS FOR HYDRAULIC ENGINEERS, H. Rouse. Standard work that gives a coherent picture of fluid mechanics from the point of view of the hydraulic engineer. Based on courses given to civil and mechanical engineering students at Columbia and the California Institute of Technology, this work covers every basic principle, method, equation, or theory of interest to the hydraulic engineer. Much of the material, diagrams, charts, etc., in this self-contained text are not duplicated elsewhere. Covers irrotational motion, conformal mapping, problems in laminar motion, fluid turbulence, flow around immersed bodies, transportation of sediment, general charcteristics of wave phenomena, gravity waves in open channels, etc. Index. Appendix of physical properties of common fluids. Frontispiece + 245 figures and photographs. xvi + 422pp. 5⅜ x 8. S729 Paperbound **$2.25**

WATERHAMMER ANALYSIS, John Parmakian. Valuable exposition of the graphical method of solving waterhammer problems by Assistant Chief Designing Engineer, U.S. Bureau of Reclamation. Discussions of rigid and elastic water column theory, velocity of waterhammer waves, theory of graphical waterhammer analysis for gate operation, closings, openings, rapid and slow movements, etc., waterhammer in pump discharge caused by power failure, waterhammer analysis for compound pipes, and numerous related problems. "With a concise and lucid style, clear printing, adequate bibliography and graphs for approximate solutions at the project stage, it fills a vacant place in waterhammer literature," WATER POWER. 43 problems. Bibliography. Index. 113 illustrations. xiv + 161pp. 5⅜ x 8½. S1061 Paperbound **$1.65**

AERODYNAMIC THEORY: A GENERAL REVIEW OF PROGRESS, William F. Durand, editor-in-chief. A monumental joint effort by the world's leading authorities prepared under a grant of the Guggenheim Fund for the Promotion of Aeronautics. Intended to provide the student and aeronautic designer with the theoretical and experimental background of aeronautics. Never equalled for breadth, depth, reliability. Contains discussions of special mathematical topics not usually taught in the engineering or technical courses. Also: an extended two-part treatise on Fluid Mechanics, discussions of aerodynamics of perfect fluids, analyses of experiments with wind tunnels, applied airfoil theory, the non-lifting system of the airplane, the air propeller, hydrodynamics of boats and floats, the aerodynamics of cooling, etc. Contributing experts include Munk, Giacomelli, Prandtl, Toussaint, Von Karman, Klemperer, among others. Unabridged republication. 6 volumes bound as 3. Total of 1,012 figures, 12 plates. Total of 2,186pp. Bibliographies. Notes. Indices. 5⅜ x 8. S328-S330 Paperbound The Set **$13.50**

APPLIED HYDRO- AND AEROMECHANICS, L. Prandtl and O. G. Tietjens. Presents, for the most part, methods which will be valuable to engineers. Covers flow in pipes, boundary layers, airfoil theory, entry conditions, turbulent flow in pipes, and the boundary layer, determining drag from measurements of pressure and velocity, etc. "Will be welcomed by all students of aerodynamics," NATURE. Unabridged, unaltered. An Engineering Society Monograph, 1934. Index. 226 figures, 28 photographic plates illustrating flow patterns. xvi + 311pp. 5⅜ x 8. S375 Paperbound **$2.00**

SUPERSONIC AERODYNAMICS, E. R. C. Miles. Valuable theoretical introduction to the supersonic domain, with emphasis on mathematical tools and principles, for practicing aerodynamicists and advanced students in aeronautical engineering. Covers fundamental theory, divergence theorem and principles of circulation, compressible flow and Helmholtz laws, the Prandtl-Busemann graphic method for 2-dimensional flow, oblique shock waves, the Taylor-Maccoll method for cones in supersonic flow, the Chaplygin method for 2-dimensional flow, etc. Problems range from practical engineering problems to development of theoretical results. "Rendered outstanding by the unprecedented scope of its contents . . . has undoubtedly filled a vital gap," AERONAUTICAL ENGINEERING REVIEW. Index. 173 problems, answers. 106 diagrams. 7 tables. xii + 255pp. 5⅜ x 8. S214 Paperbound **$1.45**

HYDRAULIC TRANSIENTS, G. R. Rich. The best text in hydraulics ever printed in English . . . by one of America's foremost engineers (former Chief Design Engineer for T.V.A.). Provides a transition from the basic differential equations of hydraulic transient theory to the arithmetic intergration computation required by practicing engineers. Sections cover Water Hammer, Turbine Speed Regulation, Stability of Governing, Water-Hammer Pressures in Pump Discharge Lines, The Differential and Restricted Orifice Surge Tanks, The Normalized Surge Tank Charts of Calame and Gaden, Navigation Locks, Surges in Power Canals—Tidal Harmonics, etc. Revised and enlarged. Author's prefaces. Index. xiv + 409pp. 5⅜ x 8½. S116 Paperbound **$2.50**

HYDRAULICS AND ITS APPLICATIONS, A. H. Gibson. Excellent comprehensive textbook for the student and thorough practical manual for the professional worker, a work of great stature in its area. Half the book is devoted to theory and half to applications and practical problems met in the field. Covers modes of motion of a fluid, critical velocity, viscous flow, eddy formation, Bernoulli's theorem, flow in converging passages, vortex motion, form of effluent streams, notches and weirs, skin friction, losses at valves and elbows, siphons, erosion of channels, jet propulsion, waves of oscillation, and over 100 similar topics. Final chapters (nearly 400 pages) cover more than 100 kinds of hydraulic machinery: Pelton wheel, speed regulators, the hydraulic ram, surge tanks, the scoop wheel, the Venturi meter, etc. A special chapter treats methods of testing theoretical hypotheses: scale models of rivers, tidal estuaries, siphon spillways, etc. 5th revised and enlarged (1952) edition. Index. Appendix. 427 photographs and diagrams. 95 examples, answers. xv + 813pp. 6 x 9. S791 Clothbound **$8.00**

FLUID MECHANICS THROUGH WORKED EXAMPLES, D. R. L. Smith and J. Houghton. Advanced text covering principles and applications to practical situations. Each chapter begins with concise summaries of fundamental ideas. 163 fully worked out examples applying principles outlined in the text. 275 other problems, with answers. Contents: The Pressure of Liquids on Surfaces; Floating Bodies; Flow Under Constant Head in Pipes; Circulation; Vorticity; The Potential Function; Laminar Flow and Lubrication; Impact of Jets; Hydraulic Turbines; Centrifugal and Reciprocating Pumps; Compressible Fluids; and many other items. Total of 438 examples. 250 line illustrations. 340pp. Index. 6 x 8⅞.   S981 Clothbound **$6.00**

THEORY OF SHIP MOTIONS, S. N. Blagoveshchensky. The only detailed text in English in a rapidly developing branch of engineering and physics, it is the work of one of the world's foremost authorities—Blagoveshchensky of Leningrad Shipbuilding Institute. A senior-level treatment written primarily for engineering students, but also of great importance to naval architects, designers, contractors, researchers in hydrodynamics, and other students. No mathematics beyond ordinary differential equations is required for understanding the text. Translated by T. & L. Strelkoff, under editorship of Louis Landweber, Iowa Institute of Hydraulic Research, under auspices of Office of Naval Research. Bibliography. Index. 231 diagrams and illustrations. Total of 649pp. 5⅜ x 8½.   Vol. I: S234 Paperbound **$2.00**
Vol. II: S235 Paperbound **$2.00**

THEORY OF FLIGHT, Richard von Mises. Remains almost unsurpassed as balanced, well-written account of fundamental fluid dynamics, and situations in which air compressibility effects are unimportant. Stressing equally theory and practice, avoiding formidable mathematical structure, it conveys a full understanding of physical phenomena and mathematical concepts. Contains perhaps the best introduction to general theory of stability. "Outstanding," Scientific, Medical, and Technical Books. New introduction by K. H. Hohenemser. Bibliographical, historical notes. Index. 408 illustrations. xvi + 620pp. 5⅜ x 8⅜.   S541 Paperbound **$3.50**

THEORY OF WING SECTIONS, I. H. Abbott, A. E. von Doenhoff. Concise compilation of subsonic aerodynamic characteristics of modern NASA wing sections, with description of their geometry, associated theory. Primarily reference work for engineers, students, it gives methods, data for using wing-section data to predict characteristics. Particularly valuable: chapters on thin wings, airfoils; complete summary of NACA's experimental observations, system of construction families of airfoils. 350pp. of tables on Basic Thickness Forms, Mean Lines, Airfoil Ordinates, Aerodynamic Characteristics of Wing Sections. Index. Bibliography. 191 illustrations. Appendix. 705pp. 5⅜ x 8.   S558 Paperbound **$3.25**

WEIGHT-STRENGTH ANALYSIS OF AIRCRAFT STRUCTURES, F. R. Shanley. Scientifically sound methods of analyzing and predicting the structural weight of aircraft and missiles. Deals directly with forces and the distances over which they must be transmitted, making it possible to develop methods by which the minimum structural weight can be determined for any material and conditions of loading. Weight equations for wing and fuselage structures. Includes author's original papers on inelastic buckling and creep buckling. "Particularly successful in presenting his analytical methods for investigating various optimum design principles," AERONAUTICAL ENGINEERING REVIEW. Enlarged bibliography. Index. 199 figures. xiv + 404pp. 5⅝ x 8⅜.   S660 Paperbound **$2.50**

Electricity

TWO-DIMENSIONAL FIELDS IN ELECTRICAL ENGINEERING, L. V. Bewley. A useful selection of typical engineering problems of interest to practicing electrical engineers. Introduces senior students to the methods and procedures of mathematical physics. Discusses theory of functions of a complex variable, two-dimensional fields of flow, general theorems of mathematical physics and their applications, conformal mapping or transformation, method of images, freehand flux plotting, etc. New preface by the author. Appendix by W. F. Kiltner. Index. Bibliography at chapter ends. xiv + 204pp. 5⅜ x 8½.   S1118 Paperbound **$1.50**

FLUX LINKAGES AND ELECTROMAGNETIC INDUCTION, L. V. Bewley. A brief, clear book which shows proper uses and corrects misconceptions of Faraday's law of electromagnetic induction in specific problems. Contents: Circuits, Turns, and Flux Linkages; Substitution of Circuits; Electromagnetic Induction; General Criteria for Electromagnetic Induction; Applications and Paradoxes; Theorem of Constant Flux Linkages. New Section: Rectangular Coil in a Varying Uniform Medium. Valuable supplement to class texts for engineering students. Corrected, enlarged edition. New preface. Bibliography in notes. 49 figures. xi + 106pp. 5⅜ x 8.   S1103 Paperbound **$1.25**

INDUCTANCE CALCULATIONS: WORKING FORMULAS AND TABLES, Frederick W. Grover. An invaluable book to everyone in electrical engineering. Provides simple single formulas to cover all the more important cases of inductance. The approach involves only those parameters that naturally enter into each situation, while extensive tables are given to permit easy interpolations. Will save the engineer and student countless hours and enable them to obtain accurate answers with minimal effort. Corrected republication of 1946 edition. 58 tables. 97 completely worked out examples. 66 figures. xiv + 286pp. 5⅜ x 8½.   S974 Paperbound **$1.85**

GASEOUS CONDUCTORS: THEORY AND ENGINEERING APPLICATIONS, J. D. Cobine. An indispensable text and reference to gaseous conduction phenomena, with the engineering viewpoint prevailing throughout. Studies the kinetic theory of gases, ionization, emission phenomena; gas breakdown, spark characteristics, glow, and discharges; engineering applications in circuit interrupters, rectifiers, light sources, etc. Separate detailed treatment of high pressure arcs (Suits); low pressure arcs (Langmuir and Tonks). Much more. "Well organized, clear, straightforward," Tonks, Review of Scientific Instruments. Index. Bibliography. 83 practice problems. 7 appendices. Over 600 figures. 58 tables. xx + 606pp. 5⅜ x 8. S442 Paperbound **$3.25**

INTRODUCTION TO THE STATISTICAL DYNAMICS OF AUTOMATIC CONTROL SYSTEMS, V. V. Solodovnikov. First English publication of text-reference covering important branch of automatic control systems—random signals; in its original edition, this was the first comprehensive treatment. Examines frequency characteristics, transfer functions, stationary random processes, determination of minimum mean-squared error, of transfer function for a finite period of observation, much more. Translation edited by J. B. Thomas, L. A. Zadeh. Index. Bibliography. Appendix. xxii + 308pp. 5⅜ x 8. S420 Paperbound **$2.35**

TENSORS FOR CIRCUITS, Gabriel Kron. A boldly original method of analyzing engineering problems, at center of sharp discussion since first introduced, now definitely proved useful in such areas as electrical and structural networks on automatic computers. Encompasses a great variety of specific problems by means of a relatively few symbolic equations. "Power and flexibility . . . becoming more widely recognized," Nature. Formerly "A Short Course in Tensor Analysis." New introduction by B. Hoffmann. Index. Over 800 diagrams. xix + 250pp. 5⅜ x 8. S534 Paperbound **$2.00**

SELECTED PAPERS ON SEMICONDUCTOR MICROWAVE ELECTRONICS, edited by Sumner N. Levine and Richard R. Kurzrok. An invaluable collection of important papers dealing with one of the most remarkable devolopments in solid-state electronics—the use of the p-n junction to achieve amplification and frequency conversion of microwave frequencies. Contents: General Survey (3 introductory papers by W. E. Danielson, R. N. Hall, and M. Tenzer); General Theory of Nonlinear Elements (3 articles by A. van der Ziel, H. E. Rowe, and Manley and Rowe); Device Fabrication and Characterization (3 pieces by Bakanowski, Cranna, and Uhlir, by McCotter, Walker and Fortini, and by S. T. Eng); Parametric Amplifiers and Frequency Multipliers (13 articles by Uhlir, Heffner and Wade, Matthaei, P. K. Tien, van der Ziel, Engelbrecht, Currie and Gould, Uenohara, Leeson and Weinreb, and others); and Tunnel Diodes (4 papers by L. Esaki, H. S. Sommers, Jr., M. E. Hines, and Yariv and Cook). Introduction. 295 Figures. xiii + 286pp. 6½ x 9¼. S1126 Paperbound **$2.50**

THE PRINCIPLES OF ELECTROMAGNETISM APPLIED TO ELECTRICAL MACHINES, B. Hague. A concise, but complete, summary of the basic principles of the magnetic field and its applications, with particular reference to the kind of phenomena which occur in electrical machines. Part I: General Theory—magnetic field of a current, electromagnetic field passing from air to iron, mechanical forces on linear conductors, etc. Part II: Application of theory to the solution of electromechanical problems—the magnetic field and mechanical forces in non-salient pole machinery, the field within slots and between salient poles, and the work of Rogowski, Roth, and Strutt. Formery titled "Electromagnetic Problems in Electrical Engineering." 2 appendices. Index. Bibliography in notes. 115 figures. xiv + 359pp. 5⅜ x 8½. S246 Paperbound **$2.25**

Mechanical engineering

DESIGN AND USE OF INSTRUMENTS AND ACCURATE MECHANISM, T. N. Whitehead. For the instrument designer, engineer; how to combine necessary mathematical abstractions with independent observation of actual facts. Partial contents: instruments & their parts, theory of errors, systematic errors, probability, short period errors, erratic errors, design precision, kinematic, semikinematic design, stiffness, planning of an instrument, human factor, etc. Index. 85 photos, diagrams. xii + 288pp. 5⅜ x 8. S270 Paperbound **$2.00**

A TREATISE ON GYROSTATICS AND ROTATIONAL MOTION: THEORY AND APPLICATIONS, Andrew Gray. Most detailed, thorough book in English, generally considered definitive study. Many problems of all sorts in full detail, or step-by-step summary. Classical problems of Bour, Lottner, etc.; later ones of great physical interest. Vibrating systems of gyrostats, earth as a top, calculation of path of axis of a top by elliptic integrals, motion of unsymmetrical top, much more. Index. 160 illus. 550pp. 5⅜ x 8. S589 Paperbound **$2.75**

MECHANICS OF THE GYROSCOPE, THE DYNAMICS OF ROTATION, R. F. Deimel, Professor of Mechanical Engineering at Stevens Institute of Technology. Elementary general treatment of dynamics of rotation, with special application of gyroscopic phenomena. No knowledge of vectors needed. Velocity of a moving curve, acceleration to a point, general equations of motion, gyroscopic horizon, free gyro, motion of discs, the damped gyro, 103 similar topics. Exercises. 75 figures. 208pp. 5⅜ x 8. S66 Paperbound **$1.75**

Technological, historical

A DIDEROT PICTORIAL ENCYCLOPEDIA OF TRADES AND INDUSTRY, Manufacturing and the Technical Arts in Plates Selected from "L'Encyclopédie ou Dictionnaire Raisonné des Sciences, des Arts, et des Métiers" of Denis Diderot. Edited with text by C. Gillispie. This first modern selection of plates from the high point of 18th century French engraving is a storehouse of valuable technological information to the historian of arts and science. Over 2000 illustrations on 485 full-page plates, most of them original size, show the trades and industries of a fascinating era in such great detail that the processes and shops might very well be reconstructed from them. The plates teem with life, with men, women, and children performing all of the thousands of operations necessary to the trades before and during the early stages of the industrial revolution. Plates are in sequence, and show general operations, closeups of difficult operations, and details of complex machinery. Such important and interesting trades and industries are illustrated as sowing, harvesting, bee-keeping, cheesemaking, operating windmills, milling flour, charcoal burning, tobacco processing, indigo, fishing, arts of war, salt extraction, mining, smelting, casting iron, steel, extracting mercury, zinc, sulphur, copper, etc., slating, tinning, silverplating, gilding, making gunpowder, cannons, bells, shoeing horses, tanning, papermaking, printing, dyeing, and more than 40 other categories. Professor Gillispie, of Princeton, supplies a full commentary on all the plates, identifying operations, tools, processes, etc. This material, presented in a lively and lucid fashion, is of great interest to the reader interested in history of science and technology. Heavy library cloth. 920pp. 9 x 12. **T421 Two volume set $18.50**

CHARLES BABBAGE AND HIS CALCULATING ENGINES, edited by P. Morrison and E. Morrison. Babbage, leading 19th century pioneer in mathematical machines and herald of modern operational research, was the true father of Harvard's relay computer Mark I. His Difference Engine and Analytical Engine were the first machines in the field. This volume contains a valuable introduction on his life and work; major excerpts from his autobiography, revealing his eccentric and unusual personality; and extensive selections from "Babbage's Calculating Engines," a compilation of hard-to-find journal articles by Babbage, the Countess of Lovelace, L. F. Menabrea, and Dionysius Lardner. 8 illustrations, Appendix of miscellaneous papers. Index. Bibliography. xxxviii + 400pp. 5⅜ x 8. **T12 Paperbound $2.00**

HISTORY OF HYDRAULICS, Hunter Rouse and Simon Ince. First history of hydraulics and hydro-dynamics available in English. Presented in readable, non-mathematical form, the text is made especially easy to follow by the many supplementary photographs, diagrams, drawings, etc. Covers the great discoveries and developments from Archimedes and Galileo to modern giants—von Mises, Prandtl, von Karman, etc. Interesting browsing for the specialist; excellent introduction for teachers and students. Discusses such milestones as the two-piston pump of Ctesibius, the aqueducts of Frontius, the anticipations of da Vinci, Stevin and the first book on hydrodynamics, experimental hydraulics of the 18th century, the 19th-century expansion of practical hydraulics and classical and applied hydrodynamics, the rise of fluid mechanics in our time, etc. 200 illustrations. Bibliographies. Index. xii + 270pp. 5¾ x 8.
S1131 Paperbound $2.00

BRIDGES AND THEIR BUILDERS, David Steinman and Sara Ruth Watson. Engineers, historians, everyone who has ever been fascinated by great spans will find this book an endless source of information and interest. Dr. Steinman, recipient of the Louis Levy medal, was one of the great bridge architects and engineers of all time, and his analysis of the great bridges of history is both authoritative and easily followed. Greek and Roman bridges, medieval bridges, Oriental bridges, modern works such as the Brooklyn Bridge and the Golden Gate Bridge, and many others are described in terms of history, constructional principles, artistry, and function. All in all this book is the most comprehensive and accurate semipopular history of bridges in print in English. New, greatly revised, enlarged edition. 23 photographs, 26 line drawings. Index. xvii + 401pp. 5⅜ x 8. **T431 Paperbound $2.00**

Prices subject to change without notice.

Dover publishes books on art, music, philosophy, literature, languages, history, social sciences, psychology, handcrafts, orientalia, puzzles and entertainments, chess, pets and gardens, books explaining science, intermediate and higher mathematics, mathematical physics, engineering, biological sciences, earth sciences, classics of science, etc. Write to:

Dept. catrr.
Dover Publications, Inc.
180 Varick Street, N.Y. 14, N.Y.